First published in this edition 1973
Published by Hubbard Press, Northbrook, Illinois 60062

Hubbard Press, 2855 Shermer Road, Northbrook, Illinois 60062
Printed in the United States of America

Library of Congress catalog card number 73-83092
ISBN 0-8331-0022-X

FABLES OF LEONARDO DA VINCI

Interpreted and
transcribed by
Bruno Nardini

Introduction by
Margaret Meek

Illustrated by
Adriana Saviozzi Mazza

Hubbard Press
Northbrook, Illinois 60062

Contents

Key to reference abbreviations can be found on the last page of book.

INTRODUCTION

Introduction

These are the stories of a great storyteller who liked nothing better than to put what he thought about things into the form of fables and legends. A fable is usually very short, and the author seems to say to his listener or his reader: "You'll see what I mean if I put it this way", and then he explains a complicated idea with an easily remembered example. Most people know Aesop's fables—the lion and the rat, the fox and the grapes, for example. Certainly Leonardo did and he used them as his models because they seemed a good way to please people and to instruct them. He knew that if his readers were to learn the lesson of the story he had to make the point quickly and well, just as you tell a joke, in terms which they could associate with their everyday lives.

Legends are stories people have known for a long time and

Left: Vinci—
the house where
Leonardo was born

Right (in order):
Lorenzo de' Medici,
known as 'The Magnificent';
Ludovico Sforza,
Duke of Milan;
Francis I, king of France

are handed down through many generations. While the outline and plot usually remain the same, the person who tells them changes the details to fit the situation in which he finds himself. There is less need to make them short as the pleasure comes from the way in which the new version is told. Leonardo used these two well-known forms to show a number of things in a new light.

Leonardo was a very great genius whose extraordinary gifts enabled him to tackle almost everything that men could do. He lived in Italy in the fifteenth century (1452–1519), a time thronged with new ideas and discoveries. His many distinguished and powerful contemporaries, some of whom commissioned work from him, included Lorenzo de' Medici, Ludovico Sforza, Duke of Milan and Francis I, king of France. He was an artist, a sculptor, a musician, a stage designer as well as an engineer who made canals. We know

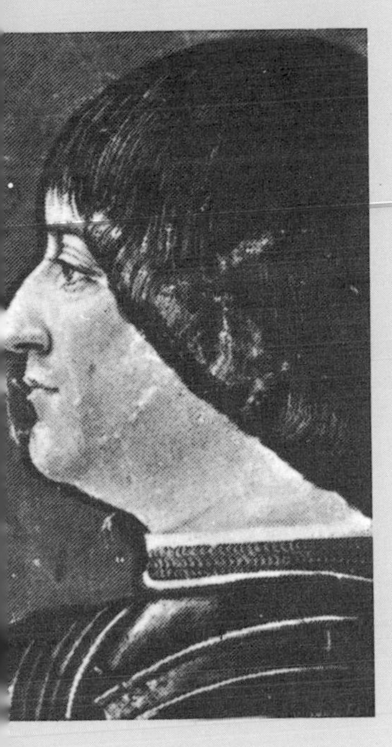

Right:
The Castle of Cloux
(or Clos-Lucé) at Amboise,
where Leonardo spent
the last years of his life

from his notebooks that he explored the workings of the human body, studied rocks and fossils, and was fascinated all his life by the movement of water and the flight of birds. His curiosity was insatiable and he differed from his contemporaries in that he took nothing for granted and trusted only what he had actually seen. In his drawings he wanted to copy that abundant beauty of nature which he loved: animals, fish, birds, flowers, stones, grass and trees, all of which occur in these stories. He looked for the ideally beautiful—the portrait of the Mona Lisa is the most famous example—and contrasted such things with the ugliness and distortions he also saw around him. Above all, he was passionate about freedom. We are told that he bought caged birds in order to have the pleasure of setting them free.

Such a man, so intense about life and so full of ideas, found it difficult to explain to his contemporaries how he felt, so he told them stories in which his observations of fig trees, cranes,

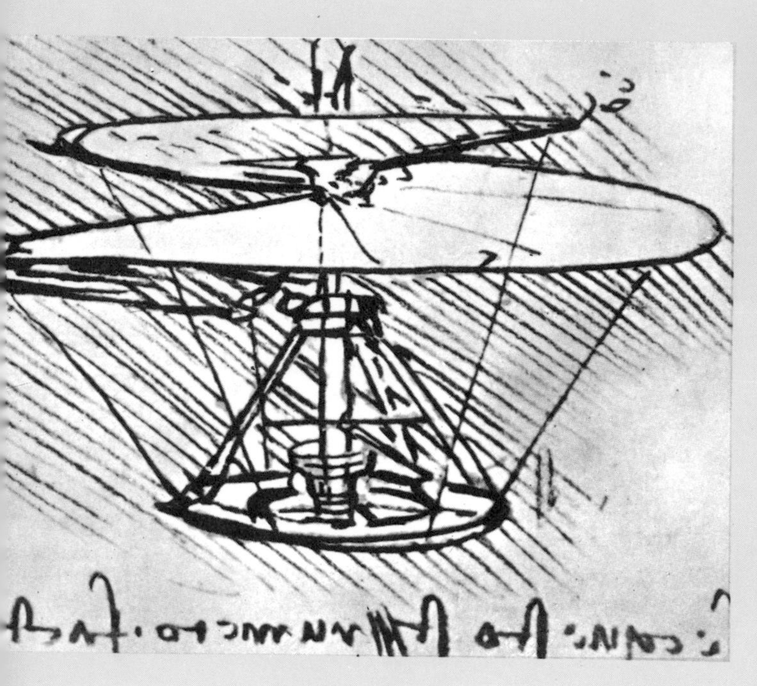

Left: study of flight, which anticipated the modern helicopter

Right: the fantastic precursor of the modern tank

grapes, lilies and, above all, water, are linked to his passions. Read the stories of the goldfinch (p. 24), the flames (p. 53), the razor (p. 54). As you read you will feel you come to know Leonardo, as he is concerned to make his listener look at things in his way, and you will recognise him as the eagle in the final story.

Because Leonardo's mind was restless and searching and his concerns were so like those of our day, we are sometimes surprised when he presents ideas which are more typical of his own period. Death was very near to people who lived when war and pestilence were common and violence could be seen everyday in the streets. Leonardo was outspoken about the corruption of courts and cities because he saw so much of it and contrasted it with the beauty of nature. But he was no sentimentalist; the animals are quite as ferocious in the stories as in real life. Sometimes the morals at the end of the tales

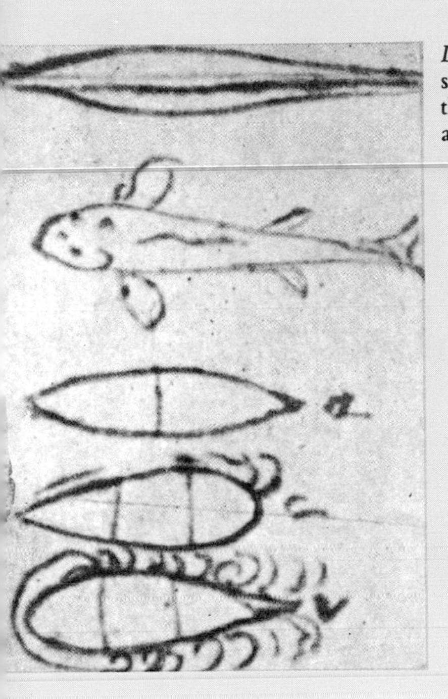

Left:
study of hydrodynamics:
the shape of the hull
and that of the fish

Right: a bombardment
of fragmented projectiles;
in modern terms—shrapnel

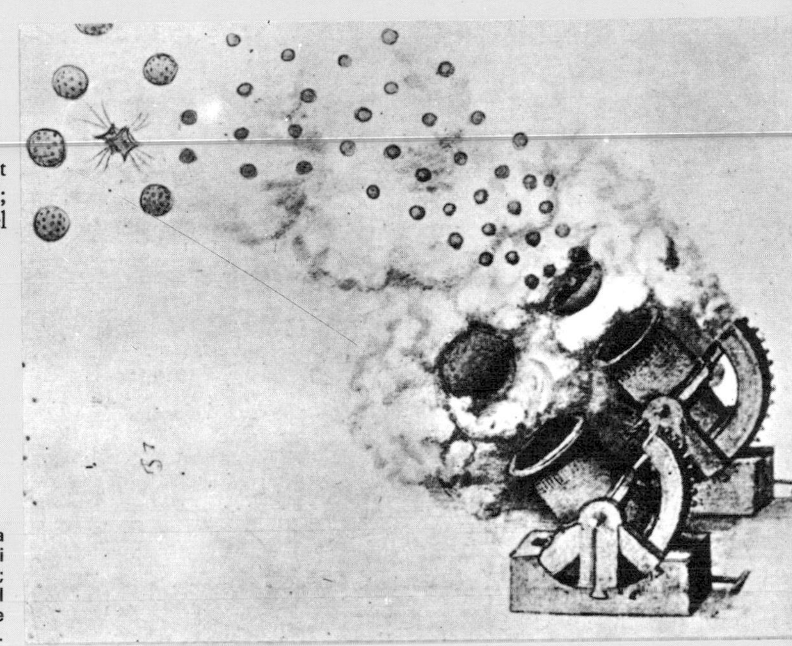

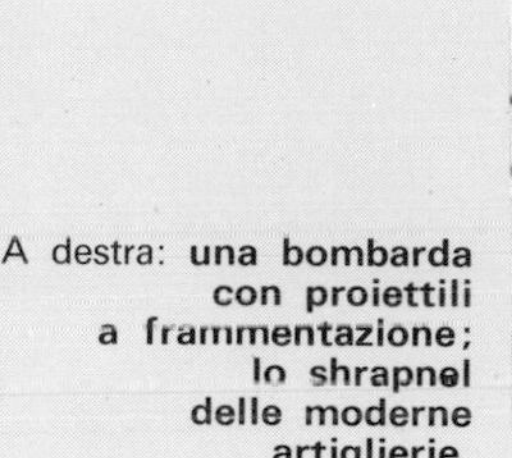

A destra: **una bombarda con proiettili a frammentazione; lo shrapnel delle moderne artiglierie.**

seem a little far-fetched ('Falsehood, like the mole, can live only if it remains hidden') but we must remember that these are not lessons for children only, but also for grown men who prided themselves on their wordly wisdom. They had probably never before heard greed described in terms of the clematis (p. 67) and that made the lesson all the more memorable.

All his life and in all his work Leonardo aimed at perfection and often saw faults in things with which others were quite content. Even in the shortest fable we feel we have been looked into by a searching eye and we hear him say:

"At last, very suddenly, there flashed forth a spark which lit a marvellous fire, with the power to do marvellous things".

MARGARET MEEK

FOREWORD

Leonardo da Vinci was a fascinating debator, a polished orator and a storyteller of originality and imagination.

His fables spread like wildfire and, as always happens with oral tradition, many different versions grew up. Some looked for the sources of Leonardo's stories in folk tales; but, with a few exceptions, they were his own.

Leonardo used small notebooks which were collected by later scholars. He wrote them in a succinct, almost telegraphic style using a strange "mirror writing" which went from right to left.

The legend of the goldfinch, which prefers to kill its children rather than see them imprisoned for life, still exists as a folk tale in the Tuscan countryside. But no one now remembers its illustrious origin. In fact, Leonardo is not generally remembered as a storyteller.

Almost five centuries have passed since Leonardo lived and all that remains of the fables, which once circulated in every court and public place in Italy and France, are a few Tuscan, Lombard and French folk tales, and the brief notes in Leonardo's manuscripts.

Bruno Nardini

FABLES

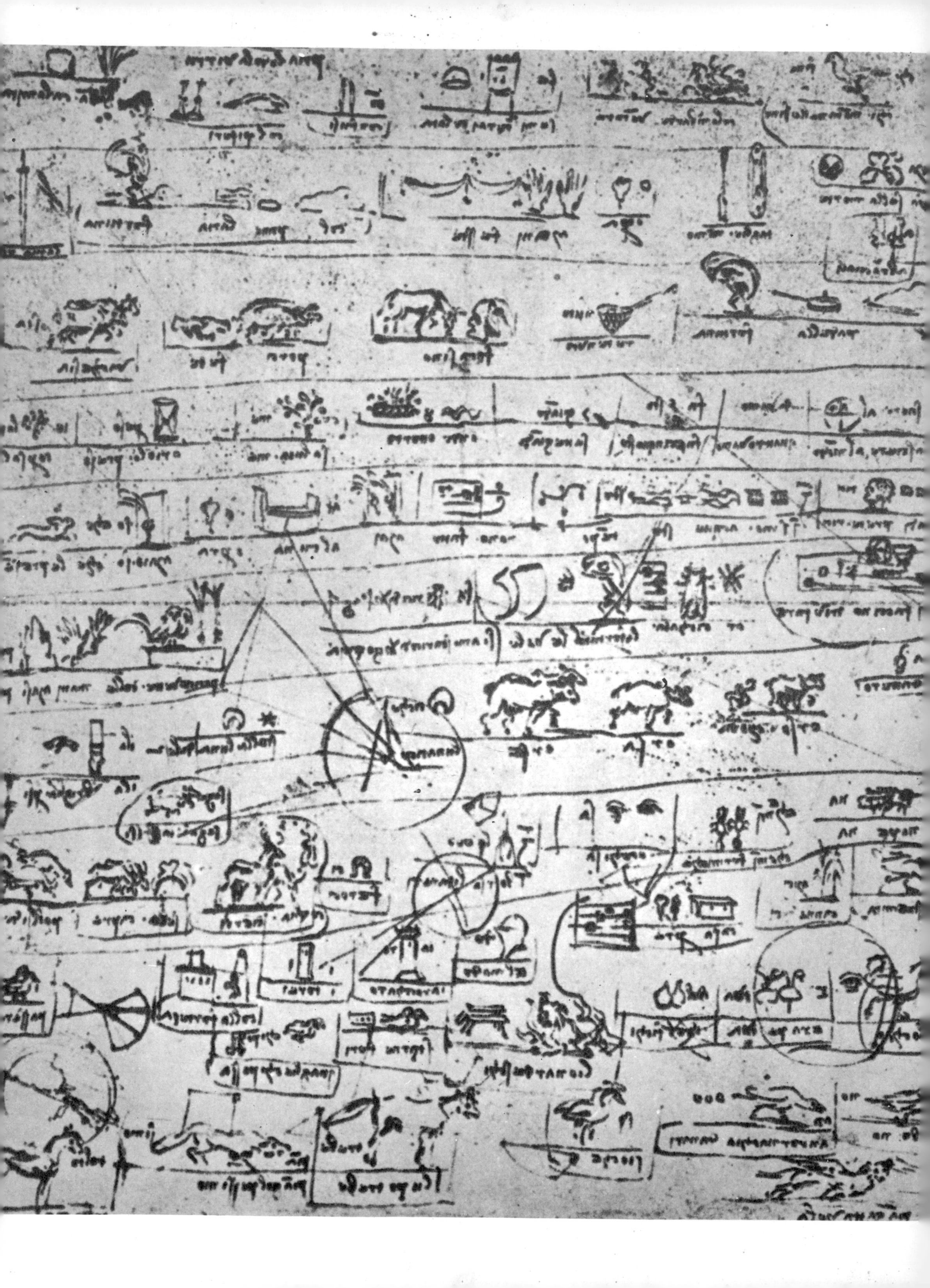

The Paper and the Ink

(from the *Fable, Fo. III.27 r.*)

One day, a sheet of paper, which was lying on a desk with other sheets just like it, found itself covered with marks. A pen, dipped in very black ink, had written a lot of words all over it.

"Could you not have spared me this humiliation?" said the piece of paper angrily to the ink. "You have sullied me with your horrible marks. You have ruined me for ever!"

"Wait!" answered the ink. "I haven't spoiled you. I have covered you with words. Now you are no longer just a piece of paper, but a message. You are the guardian of man's thoughts. You have become a precious document."

And indeed, not long afterwards, someone was tidying the desk. He collected up the sheets of paper to put them on the fire. But he suddenly noticed the sheet marked by the ink. And so he threw away the others and put back the one with the written message.

The Woodlark

(from the *Legend:* Amore di virtu. *H.5 r.*)

Once upon a time there was an old hermit who lived in a forest with only one companion, a bird of the kind called a woodlark.

One day two messengers came to see the old man, and asked him to go with them to the castle of their lord, who was gravely ill.

The old man, followed by the woodlark, went with the messengers, and was shown at once into the sick man's room.

Four doctors were shaking their heads, talking softly among themselves.

"There is no more we can do," murmured the one who seemed the most important. "Alas, he is dying."

The old hermit, standing in the doorway, was watching the woodlark, who had perched on the high window-sill and was gazing down fixedly at the sick man.

"He will recover," said the hermit.

"But how can this peasant make an assertion like that?" exclaimed the doctors all together.

The sick man opened his eyes, saw the woodlark staring at him, and tried to smile.

Little by little the colour came back to his cheeks, his strength returned, and to the astonishment of everyone present he said: "I feel a little better."

Some time later the lord of the castle, now completely recovered, went into the forest to thank the hermit.

"Do not thank me," said the hermit, "it was this bird who cured you. The woodlark," he added, "is a very sensitive bird. When he is in the presence of a sick person, if he turns away his head and will not look at him, it means there is no hope. But if he looks at the sick person, as he looked at you, it means that the patient will not die. In fact, by looking at him the woodlark helps him to recover."

Like that sensitive bird the woodlark, the love of virtue will not look at ugly, gloomy things, but seeks out all that is noble and honourable. The bird's home is the flowery woodland, and the home of virtue is the noble heart.

True love can be seen in adversity. It is like a light which shines the brightest when the night is darkest.

The Snow

(from the *Fable, Atl. 67 v.b.*)

On the summit of a very high mountain there was a rock. And on the tip of the rock there was once a flake of snow.

The snow looked at the universe around it, and began to muse to itself:

"People will say I am vain and presumptuous, and it is true! How can a little bit of snow, a mere snow-flake like me, possibly stay up here without shame? Anyone looking up at this mountain can see that all the rest of the snow is lower down. Such a scrap of snow as I am has no right to such dizzy heights, and it would be no more than I deserve if the sun treated me as he did all my comrades yesterday, and melted me with a single glance. But I shall escape the sun's righteous anger by going down to a level more fitting for something as small as me."

So saying, the little scrap of snow, hard and stiff with cold, threw itself from the rock and rolled down from the mountain peak. But the further it rolled, the bigger it became. Soon it became a great snowball, and then an avalanche. It came to rest on a hill, and the avalanche was as vast as the hill beneath it.

And so, in the summer, this was the last of the snows to melt in the sun.

This fable is for the humble, for they shall be exalted.

The Fox and the Magpie

(from the *Legend:* Falsità. *H. 9 r.*)

One day a hungry fox found himself beneath a tree on which a flock of noisy magpies was perched.

Keeping out of sight the fox began to watch them. He saw that these birds were constantly searching for food, and were not afraid even to sit on the bodies of dead animals and peck them.

"Let us try something," said the fox to himself.

Very carefully, without making a sound, he stretched himself out and lay quite still, with his mouth open as though he were dead.

Soon a magpie noticed him and at once flew down from the tree.

He approached the fox, and believing him to be dead, began to peck his tongue.

But the magpie should have been more cautious, for the fox caught him.

The Spider in the Keyhole

(from the *Fable, Atl. 299 v.b.*)

A spider, after exploring the whole house, inside and out, decided to hide in the keyhole.

What an ideal refuge, he thought. Who would ever guess he was there? And the spider could peep over the edge of the hole and look all round.

"Up there," he said to himself, glancing up at the stone lintel, "I shall spread a net for the flies. Down here," he added, looking at the step, "I shall spread another for the grubs. Here, by the side of the door, I shall set a little trap for the mosquitoes."

The spider was overjoyed. Being in the keyhole gave him a new and wonderful feeling of security. It was so narrow, dark, and lined with iron. It seemed more impregnable than a fortress, and safer than any armour.

While he was indulging in these delightful thoughts, the spider heard the sound of approaching footsteps. He crept back into the depths of his refuge.

But the spider had forgotten that the keyhole was not made for him. Its rightful possession, the key, thrust into the lock and pushed him out.

The Goldfinch

(from the *Legend:* Calderugio. *H. 63 v.*)

When she came back to her nest with a little worm in her beak, the gold-finch found her children gone. Someone had taken them while she was away.

She began to search everywhere for them, crying and calling. The whole forest resounded with her shrieks, but no one replied.

Night and day, without eating or sleeping, the goldfinch hunted for her little ones, searching every tree and looking in every nest.

One day a chaffinch said to her:

"I think I saw your children at the farmer's house."

The goldfinch went off full of hope, and soon arrived at the farmer's house. She perched on the roof, but there was no one there. She flew down into the yard—no one.

Then raising her head, she saw a cage hanging outside the window. Her children were prisoners inside it.

When they saw their mother clinging to the bars of the cage, the children began to cheep, begging her to let them out. She tried to break the bars of their prison with her beak and claws, but in vain.

Then, with a great cry of grief, she flew away.

The next day the goldfinch returned to the cage where her children were trapped. She gazed at them for a long time with great sorrow in her heart. Then she fed them through the bars one by one, for the last time.

She had brought them a poisonous herb, and the little birds died.

"Better death," she said, "than the loss of liberty."

The Peach Tree

(from the *Fable, Atl. 76 r.a.*)

A peach tree grew near a walnut tree and looked enviously at its companion's branches, laden with nuts.

"Why should that tree have so much fruit," it thought, "while I have so little? It's not fair. I am going to try to do as well."

"Do not attempt it," said a young plum tree that had read the peach tree's thoughts. "Do you not see what thick branches the walnut tree has? Do you not see that strong trunk? Each of us must give according to his ability. Think about making good peaches. It is quality that matters, not quantity."

But the peach tree, blind with jealousy, would not listen. It asked its roots to suck more nourishment from the earth, its fibres to carry more sap, its boughs to bear more blossom, and its blossom to turn to fruit, until, when harvest time came, it was laden from top to bottom with fruit.

But when the peaches ripened their weight increased, and the branches could not bear them. Nor could the trunk hold up all those fruit-laden branches. With a groan, the peach tree bent. And then, with a great crash, the trunk broke and fell. And the peaches rotted at the foot of the walnut tree.

The Lioness

(from the *Legend:* Leonessa. *H. 22 r.*)

The hunters, armed with spears and sharpened stakes, approached in silence. The lioness, suckling her cubs, caught their scent and was aware of the danger.

But it was too late. The hunters were there and about to strike.

At the sight of their weapons the lioness, terrified, almost fled. But if she had done that, she would have left her cubs to the mercy of the hunters. She decided to defend them, lowered her eyes so as not to see the menacing iron spikes that struck such terror into her heart, and with a despairing bound, leaped into the midst of the hunters.

Her great courage saved her.

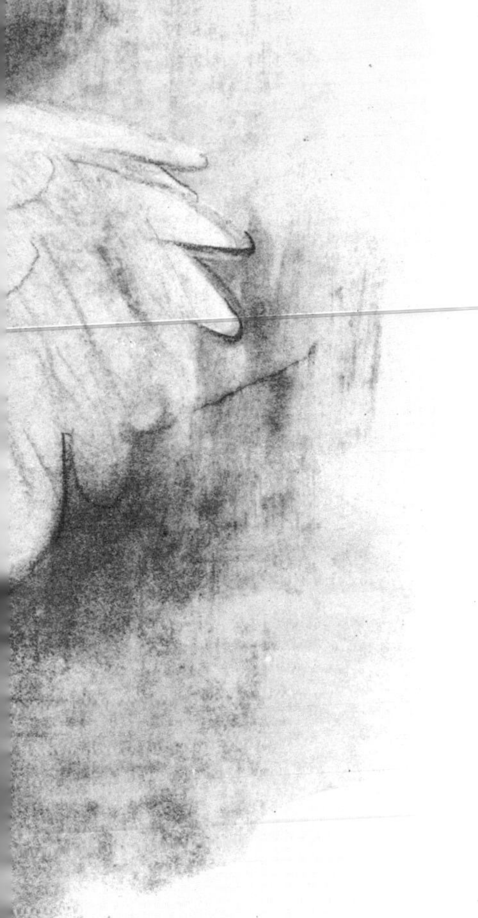

The Swan

(from the *Legend:* Cigno. *H. 13 v.*)

The swan arched his supple neck towards the water and gazed at his reflection for a long time.

He understood the reason for his weariness and for the cold that gripped his body, making him tremble as though it were winter. With absolute certainty, he knew that his hour had come and that he must prepare for death.

His feathers were still as white as they had been on the first day of his life. Seasons and years had passed without a blemish appearing on his snowy plumage. He could go now, and his life would end in beauty.

Straightening his beautiful neck, he swam slowly and majestically beneath a willow, where he had been accustomed to rest in the hot weather. It was already evening, and the sunset was touching the water of the lake with crimson and violet.

And in the great silence that was falling all around, the swan began to sing.

Never before had he found notes so full of love for all of nature, for the beauty of the heavens, the water and the earth. His sweet song rang through the air, scarcely tinged with melancholy, until, softly, softly, it faded with the last traces of light on the horizon.

"It is the swan," said the fishes, the birds, and all the beasts of woodland and meadow. Touched to the heart, they said: "The swan is dying."

The Oyster and the Crab

(from the *Legend:* Ostriga—Pel Tradimento—*H. 14 v.*)

An oyster was in love with the moon. When the full moon shone in the sky, he spent hours watching it with open mouth.

A crab saw from his observation post that the oyster was completely open at the full moon, and decided to eat him.

The following night, when the oyster opened, the crab put a pebble inside.

The oyster immediately tried to close again, but was prevented by the stone.

This happens to anyone who opens his mouth to tell his secrets. There is always an ear ready to receive them.

The Fig Tree

(from the *Fable, Atl. 76 r.a.*)

Once upon a time there was a fig tree that had no fruit. Everyone passed by without looking at it.

In spring it put forth its leaves, but in summer, when the other trees were laden with fruit, nothing at all appeared on its branches.

"I would so love to have men praise me," sighed the fig tree. "All I want is to bear fruit like the other trees."

It tried and tried again, until at last, one summer, it too was laden with fruit. The sun caused the figs to grow and swell and made them sweet and fragrant.

People noticed this. Never before had they seen a fig tree so laden with fruit. And at once it was a race to see who could pick the most. They clambered up the trunk. They bent the highest branches with sticks, and some they broke off with their weight. Everyone tried to steal the delicious figs, and very soon the poor fig tree was all bent and broken.

So: those who cry out for attention may find, to their sorrow, that they receive more than they want.

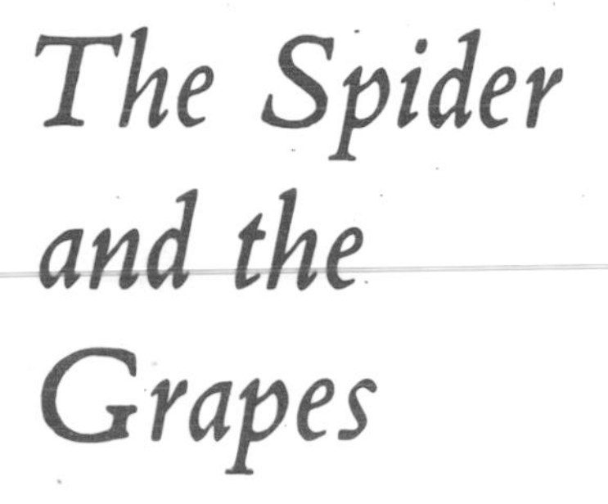

The Spider and the Grapes

(from the *Fable, Atl. 67 v.b.*)

A spider watched the movements of the insects day after day, and observed that the flies swarmed particularly round a bunch of large, very sweet grapes.

"I know what to do," he said to himself.

He climbed to the top of the vine and let himself down from there, on a fine thread, to the bunch of grapes. There he settled in a tiny space between two grapes.

From this hiding place he began to prey like a brigand upon the poor flies who came in search of food. He killed many of them, because none of them suspected that he was there.

But soon it was harvest time.

The farmer came to the field, picked the bunch of grapes and threw it into the vat, where it was at once crushed together with the other bunches.

The grapes were the fatal trap for the deceiving spider, who died just as the flies he had tricked died.

The Lily

(from the *Fable, H. 44 r.*)

On the green banks of the river Ticino a beautiful lily stood straight and tall on its stem, gazing at its white petals reflected in the water. And the water yearned to possess the lily.

Every ripple that passed carried with it the image of the lovely white flower. And the water's longing flowed back to the ripples yet to come.

And so the whole stream began to shiver, and the current became turbulent and swift. The water could not pluck the lily that stood so firmly on its tall strong stem, so it hurled itself in fury against the bank, which was washed away by the flood. And with it went that lovely, solitary flower.

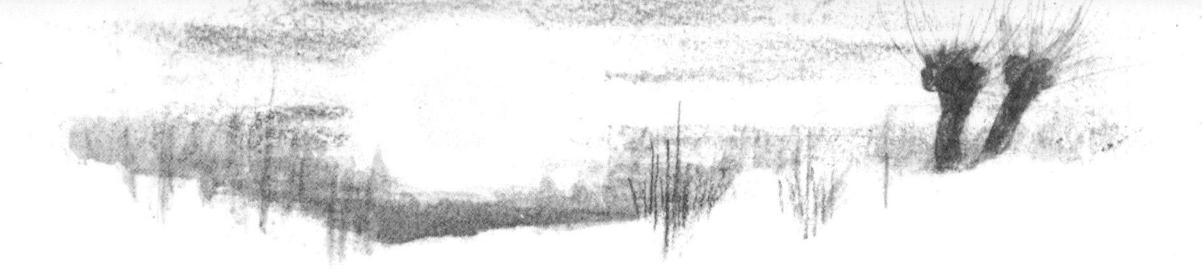

The Donkey and the Ice

(from the *Fable, Atl.* 67 *v.b.*)

Once upon a time there was a weary donkey who did not have the energy to walk as far as his stable.

It was winter, and very cold. All the streets were covered with ice.

"I am going to stop here," said the donkey, sinking to the ground.

A hungry little sparrow fluttered down beside him and whispered in his ear:

"Donkey, you are not in the street, but on a frozen lake. Take care."

The donkey was tired out. He ignored the warning. He gave a great yawn and fell asleep.

The warmth of his body began little by little to melt the ice, until, with a crash, the ice broke.

When he found himself in the water, the donkey woke in terror. And as he swam through the icy water, he wished he had listened to the friendly sparrow.

The Laurel and the Myrtle

(from the *Fable, Atl. 67 r.d.*)

Two peasants with hatchets in their hands stopped beside the pear tree.

"Pear tree," called the laurel, "they are coming for you!"

And, indeed, the peasants began to strike heavy blows with their hatchets at the foot of the tree.

"Pear tree," called the myrtle, "where are you going? Where is all the pride you felt when your boughs were laden with fruit?"

"After this," added the laurel, "you will not shade us any more with your thick tresses."

The pear tree, mortally wounded, murmured:

"I am going away with these peasants. Now they are cutting off my branches, and they will take me to a famous sculptor's studio. He will carve me into the shape of the god Jupiter, and then I shall be carried into a temple built especially for me, and all men will worship me. And you, laurel, and you, myrtle, will often find your boughs broken and leafless, because men will come and pick your branches to crown me and honour me as befits a god."

The Camel

(from the *Legend:* Camelli, *H. 23 r.*)

The camel, kneeling, waited patiently for his master to finish loading him.
One sack, two sacks, three, four . . .
"When is he going to stop?" the camel said to himself.
Finally the man clicked his tongue and the camel stood up.
"Let us go," said the master, pulling on the bridle. But the camel did not move.

"Come on!" cried the man, jerking the rope. But the camel dug in his feet and stayed where he was.

"I see," said his master, and with a sigh he took two sacks down from the camel's back.

"That, I think, is a fair weight," murmured the camel to himself, and at once began to move.

They walked all day at a good speed, and the man thought they would be able to reach the village. But at a certain point the camel stopped.

"Courage," said the master, "only a few more miles and we are there." The camel's only response was to lie down on the ground.

"My legs tell me," he said to himself, "that we have walked enough for today."

And the man was obliged to unload and to camp beside the camel in the desert.

The Tongue and the Teeth

(from the *Fable, Atl. 67 v.a.*)

Once upon a time there was a boy who had the bad habit of talking more than necessary.

"What a tongue!" sighed the teeth one day. "It is never still, never quiet!"

"What are you grumbling about?" replied the tongue arrogantly. "You teeth are only slaves, and your job is merely to chew whatever I decide. We have nothing in common, and I shall not allow you to meddle with my affairs."

So the boy went on chattering, very impertinently sometimes, and his tongue was happy, learning new words every day.

But one day, when the boy did some damage, and then allowed his tongue to tell a big lie, the teeth obeyed the heart, sprang together and bit the tongue.

From that day on the tongue became timid and prudent, and thought twice before speaking.

The Oyster and the Mouse

(from the *Fable, H. 51 v.*)

An oyster found himself, together with a large number of fish, in a fisherman's house not far from the sea.

"We shall all die here," thought the oyster, looking at his companions as they lay gasping, scattered over the floor.

A mouse passed by.

"Listen, mouse!" said the oyster. "Would you kindly carry me to the sea?"

"Certainly," replied the mouse, who had decided to eat the oyster, "but you must open your shell, because I cannot carry you closed like that."

The oyster opened cautiously, and the deceitful mouse immediately thrust in his muzzle to take a bite.

But the oyster was no fool. He snapped his shell shut, giving the lying mouse a rap on the head.

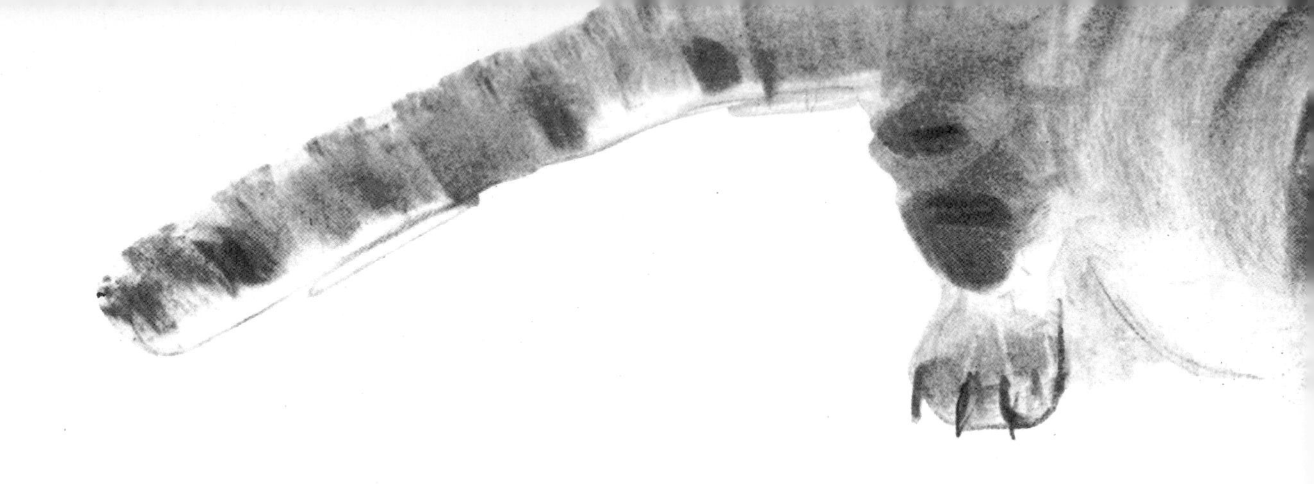

A Mouse, A Weasel and A Cat

(from the *Fable, Atl. 67 v.a.*)

One morning a little mouse could not leave his house. It was besieged.

A hungry weasel was waiting outside. Through a tiny breathing hole the mouse saw him intently watching the entrance, ready to spring.

The poor little mouse, knowing himself to be in terrible danger, trembled all over with fear.

But a cat suddenly leaped on to the weasel's back, seized him between his teeth and devoured him.

"Great Jupiter, I thank you!" sighed the mouse, who had observed the scene through his spy hole, "and I shall willingly sacrifice some of my food to you."

And so he gave the cat some of his food. But in escaping one danger, he foolishly forgot the other. The cat, being a cat, ate him too.

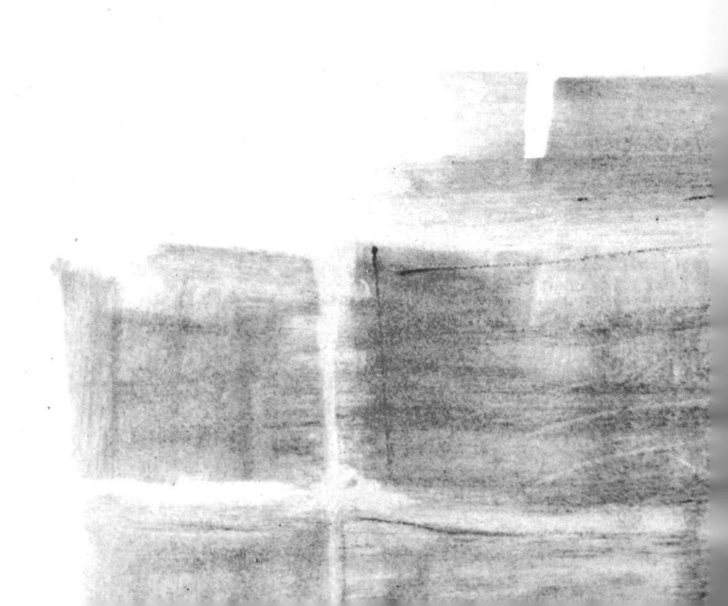

The Cranes

(from the *Legend:* Fedeltà over Lealtà. *H. 9 r.*)

The king was a good king, but he had many enemies. The cranes, loyal and faithful, were anxious for him. It was always possible, especially at night, that enemies might surround the palace and take the king prisoner.

"What shall we do?" they wondered. "The soldiers, who ought to be on guard, are sleeping. No more tasks can be laid on the dogs, for they are always hunting and always tired. It is for us to guard the palace and let our king sleep peacefully."

So the cranes decided to become sentinels. They divided themselves into groups, and each had his own beat, with regular changes of the guard.

The largest group strung itself out in the meadow surrounding the palace. Another group stood outside all the doors. And a third decided to stay in the king's bedroom, so as to watch him all the time.

"And suppose we are overcome by sleep?" some of them asked.

"We have a safeguard against falling asleep," replied the oldest crane. "We shall all grasp a stone in the claw which is raised when we are standing still. If one of us goes to sleep, the stone will fall to the ground and the noise will wake him.

Every night since then the cranes have been guarding the palace, changing every two hours. And not one has yet dropped his stone.

The Elephant

(from the *Legend:* Leofante. *H. 19 r.- 20 v.*)

The great elephant has, by nature, qualities which are very rare among men —honesty, prudence and justice.

Elephants are religious, and show it every time the new moon appears. As a ceremonial greeting they go down to the river and wash for a long time.

When they are ill, they lie down on the ground, and gather flowers and herbs with their trunks, flinging them up to the sky as though they were making an offering to the gods.

When the old elephants lose their tusks, they bury them.

Usually elephants use one tusk for digging up roots for food, and keep the other for fighting.

When they are surrounded by hunters, and realise that they are too tired to resist any longer, they strike their tusks against the trees until they break off. They know that men kill them only for their tusks, and by doing this they save their lives.

They are merciful with their victims, and recognise every danger in advance.

One day an elephant found a man alone and lost in the forest. He went up to the man, obviously inviting him to follow and so helped him to find his way. Another day he saw only footprints, so, fearing an ambush, he halted, panting, and showed the marks to his companions. They advanced all together, one pressed against the other, very cautiously.

They usually live in herds, with the eldest always walking at the head and the next eldest at the end.

They are very modest, and couple only at night and in secret. Afterwards they return to the herd, first washing themselves in the river.

They never fight for their mates as many other animals do, and they are kind to the weakest. If they meet a flock or herd or other animals they make a way through with their trunks so as to disturb no one. And they do not react unless provoked.

An elephant once fell into a pit. All the elephants in the herd began to throw branches and stones into the hole to raise the bottom and help the captive elephant to climb out.

When they hear pigs squealing they are afraid, and retreat in disorder, injuring more of their own comrades than of the enemy.

They love rivers,
and wander continually around them.
But because they are so heavy,
they cannot swim. They eat stones,
but their favourite food is the trunks of trees.
They hate mice. Flies, on the other hand,
are attracted by their smell.
But when the elephants feel the flies on them,
they wrinkle their skin and kill them all.
If they have to cross a river they send the babies
further downstream, while the adults remain
upstream, making a dam with their great bodies
to break the current and prevent the water from
carrying their children away.

The dragon is the enemy of the elephant. He attacks by sliding under the elephant's belly. He binds the elephant's feet with his tail. With his wings and spikes he grips the elephant round the body.

But when the elephant falls, he crushes the dragon. And so, dying, he revenges himself on his killer.

The Chestnut and the Fig Tree

(from the *Fable, Atl. 67 r.a.*)

One day an old chestnut tree saw a man up a fig tree.

The man was bending the branches towards himself, pulling off the ripe figs. He put them one by one into his mouth, and broke them up with his strong teeth.

And the chestnut tree's murmuring branches said:

"Oh fig tree, how much less you owe to Mother Nature than I! Do you see what she has done for me? How well she has arranged and protected my dear children, dressing them first in a robe of fine material, over which she put a coat of hard skin, softly lined. And not satisfied with having done me this kindness, she has built for each of them a strong little house, and furnished it with sharp thick spines to protect it from the hands of men."

When the fig tree, with all its figs, heard this, it began to laugh, and after laughing for a time, it said:

"But do you really know man? Whatever you do he will go to great trouble to take all your fruit from you. Armed with rods, sticks and stones, he will strike your branches and make your fruit shower down. And once they have fallen he will stamp on them or crush them with stones to force them out of their little houses, so well protected with spines. And your children will come out battered, broken and maimed.

But my fruit is gathered delicately and I am touched only by hands."

The Tree and the Pole

(from the *Fable, Fo. III. 47 v.*)

A tree which grew luxuriantly, lifting to heaven its plume of tender leaves, objected to the presence of a straight, dry old pole beside it.

"Pole, you are too close to me. Can you not move further away?"

The pole pretended not to hear, and made no reply.

Then the tree turned to the thorn hedge surrounding it.

"Hedge, can you not go somewhere else? You irritate me."

The hedge pretended not to hear, and made no reply.

"Beautiful tree," said a lizard, raising his wise little head to look up at the tree, "do you not see that the pole is holding you straight? Do you not realise that the hedge is protecting you from bad company?"

The Ibis

(from the *Legend:* Ibis. *H. 26 v.*)

A rascally young ibis, once he had learned to run and fly, never stopped. He was constantly in search of food, and ate everything he found.

But one morning the young ibis stayed in the nest. He had a temperature and a terrible stomach ache.

His mother was frightened and ran to him immediately, looked at him, felt him with her beak and claws, and said:

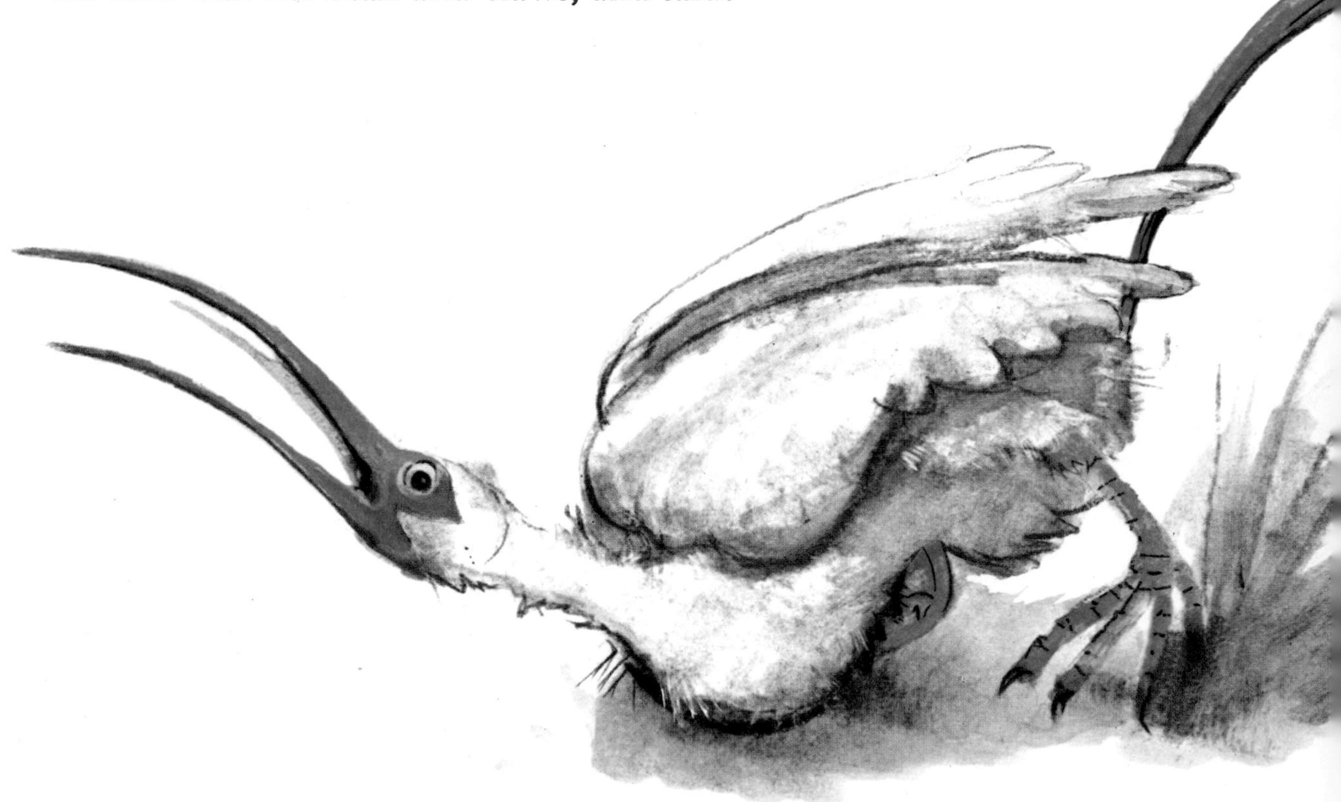

"I see. You have eaten something you should not, because you are so greedy, and now it has made you ill."

With these words the mother ibis flew to the pond and filled her crop with water. Returning to the nest she gave him some of the water to relieve his discomfort.

Reproduction of a section of the manuscript containing the fable "Le Fiamme"

The Flames

(from the *Fable, Atl. 67 r.b.*)

For more than a month the flames had glowed in the glass-blower's furnace, where bottles and glasses were made.

One day they saw a candle supported on a fine shining candlestick coming towards them. At once, with passionate longing, they strove to approach the sweet little candle.

One in particular, leaping from the ember that fed it, turned its back on the furnace, and slipping through a little crack, flung itself upon the candle, devouring it greedily.

But the eager flame soon consumed the poor candle and, not wishing to die with it, tried to return to the furnace from which it had escaped.

But it could not detach itself from the soft wax, and it called in vain for help from the other flames.

The rebel flame turned into suffocating smoke, leaving all its brothers resplendent, looking forward to a long and glittering life.

The Razor

(from the *Fable, Atl. 175 v.a.*)

Once upon a time there was a fine razor in a barber's shop. One day when there was no one in the shop, it decided to have a look round. It slipped its blade out of the handle and went outside to enjoy the beautiful spring day.

When the razor saw the sun reflected from itself, it was surprised and enraptured. The steel blade threw out such dazzling beams that suddenly, in an excess of pride, the razor said to itself:

"And must I go back into that shop from which I have only just escaped? Certainly not! The gods cannot wish that such beauty as mine should be thus defiled. It would be madness to stay here and cut these yokels' soapy beards, repeating the same mechanical operations for ever and ever! Is this fine body of mine really made for such work? Indeed no! So I am going to hide myself in some secret place and spend the rest of my days in peace."

So saying, the razor sought a hiding place where no one could see it.

Months passed. One day the razor felt it would like a little air. So it crept cautiously out of its refuge, and looked at itself.

Alas, what had happened? The blade had grown ugly, like a rusty saw, and no longer reflected the sunlight.

The razor was sorry for what it had done, and bitterly mourned its irreparable loss, saying:

"Oh, how much better I should have done to keep my beautiful sharp blade in trim by cutting soapy beards! My surface would still have been shining and my edge fine. And now here I am, eaten away and encrusted with hideous rust! And there is nothing to be done!"

The razor's sad end is one that comes to clever people who prefer laziness to the use of their talents. They too, like the razor, lose the sparkle and the sharp edge of their intellect, and are soon eaten away with the rust of ignorance.

The Lion

(from the *Legend:* Lione. *H. 18 r.*)

The cubs had not yet opened their eyes. They had lain for three days between the mother lioness's paws, moving only to grope for milk, hearing and seeing nothing.

A little apart, the lion proudly watched them.

Suddenly he stood up, and shaking his beautiful mane gave vent to a roar like thunder.

The cubs at once opened their eyes, while all the wild animals of the jungle fled in terror.

As the lion wakens his children with a loud cry, so praise awakens the sleeping virtue of our sons. It encourages them to study and to strive for honour, and puts to flight everything that is unworthy of them.

The Pelican

(from the *Legend:* Pelicano. *H. 13 r.*)

When the pelican went in search of food, a snake, hidden among the branches, began to move towards the nest.

The babies were sleeping peacefully.

The snake approached, and with a wicked gleam in his eyes began the kill. A poisonous bite to each, and the poor little creatures passed directly from sleep to death.

Satisfied, the snake returned to his hiding place to gloat over the pelican's return.

And in fact the bird came back shortly afterwards.

At the sight of such carnage she began to weep, and her lament was so despairing that all the inhabitants of the forest heard it and grieved.

"What meaning has my life without you?" said the poor bird, gazing on her dead children. "I want to die with you!"

And she began to peck with her beak at her breast, just over the heart. The blood gushed out of the wound and poured over the baby birds killed by the snake.

But all at once the dying pelican gave a start. Her warm blood had restored life to her children. Her love had revived them. And then, happy at last, she herself died.

The Ant and the Grain of Wheat

(from the *Fable, Atl. 67 v.b.*)

A grain of wheat, left alone in the field after the harvest, was waiting for the rain so that it could hide once more beneath the soil.

An ant saw the grain, loaded it on to his back, and plodded away painfully towards his distant ant hill.

He walked and walked, and the grain of wheat seemed to grow heavier and heavier on his weary shoulders.

"Why do you not leave me here?" said the grain of wheat.

The ant replied: "If I leave you behind, we may not have enough provisions for this winter. We ants are so many, and we each have to bring to the common larder whatever food we can find."

"But I am not made only to be eaten," went on the grain of wheat. "I am a seed, full of life, and it is my destiny to give birth to a plant. Listen, dear ant, let us make a pact."

The ant, glad to rest a little, put down the grain of wheat and asked:

"What pact?"

"If you leave me here in my field," said the grain of wheat "and do not take me to your nest, I shall give back to you, after a year, a hundred grains just like me."

The ant stared at the grain incredulously.

"Yes dear ant. Believe what I am telling you. If you give me up today I shall give you a hundred of me – a hundred grains of wheat for your nest."

The ant thought: "A hundred grains in exchange for one—but that is a miracle!"

"And how will you do that?" he asked the grain of wheat.

"That is a mystery," replied the grain of wheat. "It is the mystery of life. Dig a little hole, bury me in it, and return after a year."

The following year the ant returned. The grain of wheat had grown a new plant laden with seeds, and so kept its promise.

The Stream

(from the *Fable, Ar. 42 v.*)

A mountain stream, forgetting that it owed its water to the rain and the little brooks, decided to swell until it became as big as a river.

So it began to dash itself violently against its banks, noisily tearing away soil and stones in order to widen its bed.

But when the rain stopped, the waters shrank. The poor stream found itself caught among the stones it had torn from its banks, and was forced with much labour to hew itself a new path down into the valley.

Moral: He who wants too much gets nothing.

The Bramble

(from the *Fable. Atl. 67 r.a.*)

The poor bramble could bear it no longer. Now that its branches were covered once again with blackberries, the cheeky blackbirds were pecking and tearing all its twigs with beak and claws.

"Please," begged the bramble, turning to the most troublesome blackbird, "at least spare my leaves! I know you like my berries very much. They are your favourite fruit. But do not deprive me of the shade of my leaves, which protect me from the burning rays of the sun. And do not flay me with your claws, do not strip me of my tender bark."

To these words the blackbird, offended, replied:

"Silence, you bumpkin! Do you not know that nature made you produce these fruits simply to feed me? Do you not see that you were born only to provide my food? Do you not know, you ill-bred lout, that next winter all you will feed will be the fire?"

The bramble, hearing these words, began to weep silently.

Some time afterwards the insolent blackbird fell into a trap set by a man. In order to make a cage for the bird, the man cut branches from the hedges, and it fell to the bramble to furnish the bars.

"Oh blackbird," said the bramble, "I am still here. You used to torture me when you were free, and now it is my branches that deprive you of your freedom. I am not yet consumed by the fire as you said I would be. You have not seen me burned, but I see you imprisoned."

The Wolf

(from the *Legend:* Correzione. *H. 7 v.*)

Carefully, warily, the wolf came down out of the forest one night, attracted by the smell of a flock of sheep. With slow steps he drew near to the sheep-fold, placing his feet with the utmost caution so as not to make the slightest sound which might disturb the sleeping dog.

But one careless paw stepped on a board, the board creaked and woke the dog. The wolf had to run away, unfed and hungry. And so because of one careless foot, the whole animal suffered.

The Net

(from the *Fable. Ar. 42 v.*)

That day, like every other day, the net came up full of fish. Carp, barbel, lampreys, roach, tench, eels and many, many others ended up in the fishermen's baskets.

Deep down in the water of the river, the survivors, frightened and dismayed, did not dare to move. Whole families had already been sent to market. Entire shoals had fallen into the net and finished up in the frying pan.

What was to be done?

A few young gudgeons met behind a rock and decided to rebel.

"It is a matter of life and death," they said. "This net goes down into the water every day, in a different place each time, to take us prisoner and snatch us away from our home. It will kill us all, and the river will be empty of fish. Our children have a right to live, and we must do something to save them from this scourge."

"And what can we do?" asked a tench who had followed the conspirators.

"Destroy the net," replied the young gudgeons with one voice.

The wriggling eels swiftly carried the news of this brave decision along the river, inviting all the fishes to meet the following morning in an inlet protected by tall willows.

The next day millions of fish, of all sizes and all ages, met together to declare war on the net.

The leadership of the operation was entrusted to a clever old carp, who had twice succeeded in escaping from prison by biting through the meshes of the net.

"Listen carefully," said the carp. "The net is as wide as the river, and every mesh had a lead weight on the underside to pull it down to the bottom. Divide yourself into two groups. One group will lift the lead weights and carry them up to the surface, and the other group will hold the meshes very firmly from above. The lampreys will sever with their teeth the cord that holds the net stretched between the two banks. The eels will make an immedi-

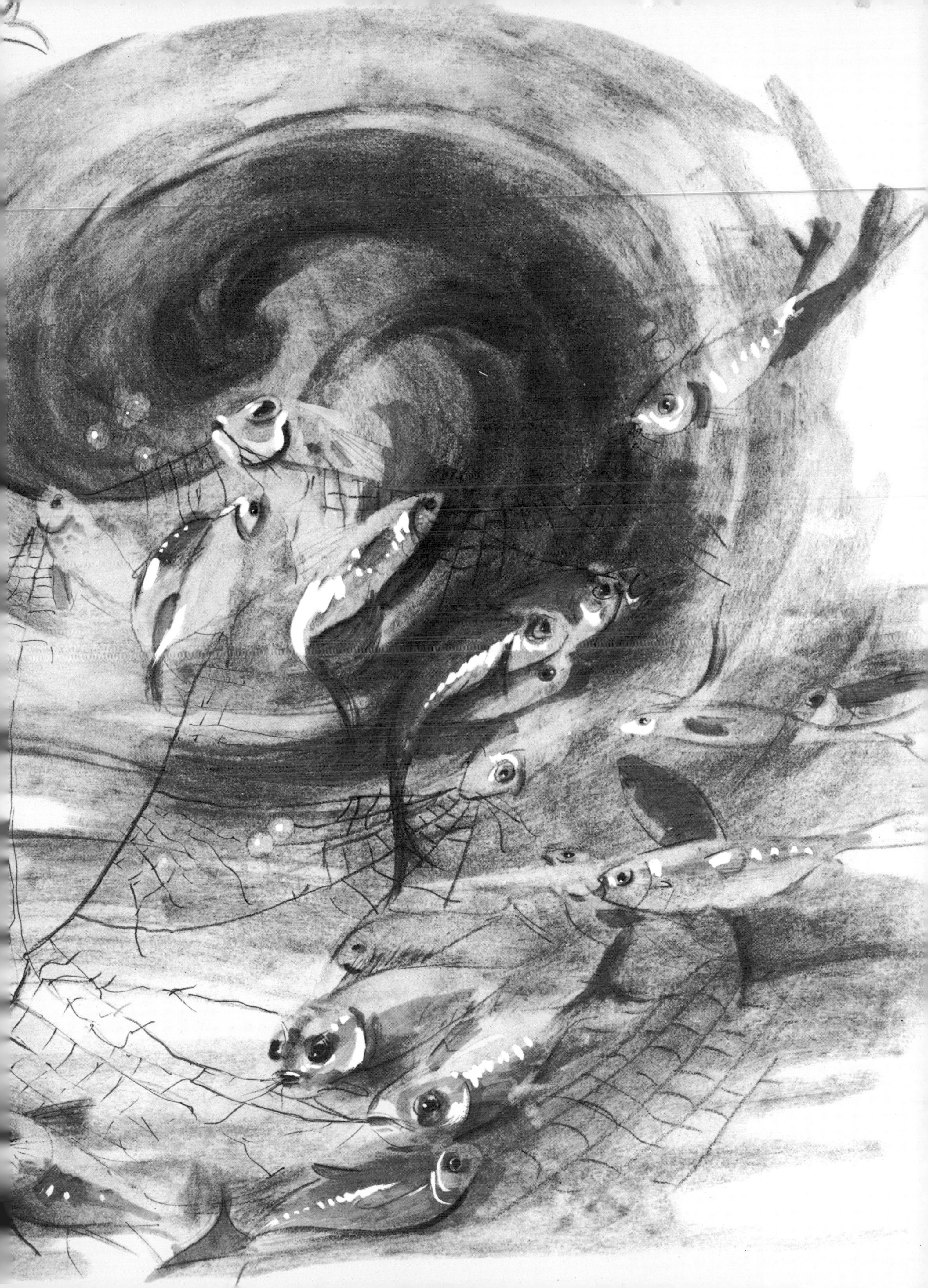

ate reconnaissance and tell us where the net has been cast."

The eels went off. The fish formed up in their groups along the margins. The gudgeon encouraged the more timid ones, reminding them of the sad end of many of their friends, and exhorting them not to be afraid of remaining entangled in the net, because no man would now be able to draw it to the bank.

The eel scouts returned. The net had been cast and was now a mile away.

Then all the fish, like a huge fleet, set sail behind the old carp.

"Take care," said the carp, "the current could drag you into the net. Slow down, and use your fins well."

And the net appeared, grey and sinister.

The fish, overcome by a sudden furious rage, swam to the attack.

The net was raised from the bottom, the ropes that held it were severed, the meshes were torn apart. But the infuriated fish would not let go of their prey. Each one of them held his piece of mesh in his mouth, and furiously waving fins and tails, they pulled in every direction to tear and destroy the net. And the water seemed to boil as the fish made their river free from danger at last.

The Clematis

(from the *Fable, Atl.* 67 *v.b.*)

In the shade of the hedge, the clematis twined its green arms round the trunks and branches of the hawthorn.

When it reached the top it looked around and saw another hedge bordering the other side of the road.

"Oh, how I should love to go over there," said the clematis. "That hedge is bigger and more beautiful than this one."

And a little at a time, stretching out its arms, it crept closer and closer to the opposite hedge. At last it reached it, caught one of the branches and began happily to wrap itself there.

But shortly after, travellers walking along the road were suddenly faced with this branch of clematis blocking their way. They seized it in their hands, tore it from the hedge and flung it into the ditch. In its greed the clematis had not seen the danger.

The Butterfly and the Flame

(from the *Fable, Atl. 257 r.b.–Atl. 67 r.a.*)

A multi-coloured butterfly was flying aimlessly through the dark one evening when he saw a point of light in the distance. At once he flew in that direction, and when he came near to the flame he fluttered round it, looking at it with wonder. How beautiful it was!

Not content with admiring it, the butterfly thought he would do what he did with fragrant flowers. He flew away, flew back, then bravely made for the flame and skimmed over it.

He found himself lying stunned beneath the light, and was stupefied to see that the points of his wings were singed.

"What has happened to me?" he wondered, but could find no reason. He could not possibly believe that a thing as beautiful as that flame could do him any harm. And so, after gathering a little strength, he shook his wings and took flight once more.

He circled a little, and again made for the flame, intending to settle on it. And at once he fell, burned, into the oil that fed the bright little flame.

"Accursed light," murmured the dying butterfly, "I thought I should find happiness in you, and instead I have found death. I regret my foolish longing, for I realised too late, and to my undoing, how dangerous you were."

"Poor butterfly," replied the flame, "I am not the sun, as you so foolishly thought. I am only a light. And those who cannot approach me prudently are burned."

This fable is meant for those who, like the butterfly, are attracted by wordly pleasures without knowing their true nature. Then, by the time they realise what they have lost, it is already too late.

The Ermine

(from the *Legend:* Moderanza. *H. 12 v.*)

A fox was having a meal, when an elegant ermine passed by. "Would you care to help yourself?" invited the fox, who had eaten enough.

"No thank you," replied the ermine, "I have already eaten."

"Ha, ha!" laughed the fox. "You ermines are the most prudish animals in the world. You eat only once a day, and you would go without rather than dirty your fur."

At that moment some hunters came up. The fox, quick as lightning, hid underground, and the ermine, no less swift than the fox, ran for his den.

But the sun had melted the snow, and his den had become a quagmire. The snow white ermine was afraid of slipping into the mud, and stopped, hesitant. And the hunters caught him.

Moderation checks all vices. The ermine was too vain about his appearance, and so lost his liberty.

The Flea and the Sheep

(from the *Fable. Atl. 119 r.a.*)

A flea, who lived in the smooth hair of a dog, one day noticed the pleasant smell of wool.

"What is going on?"

He gave a little jump and saw that his dog had gone to sleep leaning against the fleece of a sheep.

"That fleece is exactly what I need," said the flea. "It is thicker and softer, and above all safer. There is no risk of meeting the dog's claws and teeth which go in search of me every now and then. And the sheep's wool will certainly feel more pleasant."

So without thinking too much about it, the flea moved house, leaping from the dog's coat to the sheep's fleece. But the wool was thick, so thick and dense that it was not easy to penetrate to the skin.

He tried and tried, patiently separating one strand from another, and laboriously making a way through. At last he reached the roots of the hair. But they were so close together that they practically touched. The flea had not even a tiny hole through which to attack the skin.

Tired, bathed in sweat and bitterly disappointed, the flea resigned himself to going back to the dog. But the dog had gone away.

Poor flea! He wept for days and days with regret for his mistake.

The Water

(from the *Fable, Fo. III. 2 r.*)

One day, some water was seized by the wish to leave its usual place in the beautiful sea, and fly up into the sky.

So the water turned to the fire begging for help. The fire agreed, and with its heat turned the water into a thin vapour, making it lighter than air.

The vapour soared up into the sky, higher and higher, until finally it reached the coldest and most rarified level of the atmosphere. Then the water particles, numb with cold, were forced together and became once more heavier than the air. And they fell—in the form of rain. They did not just fall, they cascaded earthwards!

The arrogant water was soaked up by the dry soil and, paying heavily for its arrogance, remained imprisoned in the earth.

The Peasant and the Vine

(from the *Fable, H. 112 v.*)

"The farmer is very fond of me," thought the vine, as the peasant propped it up with a large number of poles, and held up all its branches with other supports. "I must reward him with my grapes."

So the vine set diligently to work and produced a fine crop of grapes.

But after the harvest, the farmer suddenly took out all the props and other supports and piled them up on one side. With nothing to lean on, the poor vine fell to the ground.

The farmer broke up the poles with his hatchet, carried them into the house and flung them on the fire.

Then the vine realised that the farmer didn't care for him at all. He had only helped the vine when it profited himself.

The Stone and the Steel

(from the *Fable, Atl. 257 r.b.*)

One day a flint stone struck by the steel turned upon it, surprised and indignant, and said:

"What's the matter with you? You must have taken me for someone else, because I do not know you. Let me alone, for I have never done any harm to anybody!"

The steel looked at the stone, then smiled and answered: "If you will have a little patience, you will see what marvellous fruit I can bring forth from you."

At these words the flint was comforted, and bore with great patience the blows which the steel inflicted upon it. At last, very suddenly, there flashed forth a spark which lit a marvellous fire, with the power to do wonderful things.

This fable is meant for those who begin their studies unwillingly, despite exhortations to continue. But if they are patient and persistent, they will see marvellous results.

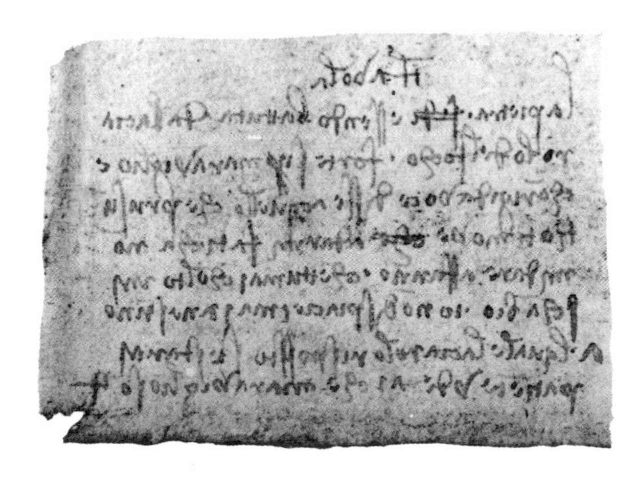

The story of The Stone and the Steel
in Leonardo's own notes

The Peacock

(from the *Legend:* Vanagloria. *H. 10 r.*)

The farmer went out, shutting the farmyard gate.

He had intended to return at once, but days passed, and still he did not appear.

The farmyard animals were hungry and thirsty. Even the cock stopped crowing.

They all stood motionless, so as not to waste their strength, in the shade of a tree.

Only the peacock rose staggeringly to his feet, opened like a fan his great multi-coloured tail, and began to pace to and fro.

"Mamma," a skinny little chicken asked the hen, "why does the peacock spread his tail every day?"

"Because he is vain, my child. And vanity is a vice that disappears only with death."

The Miser

(from the *Legend:* Avarizia. *H. 6 v.*)

Every now and again the toad opened his mouth and swallowed a little earth.

"Why are you so thin?" a ladybird asked him one day.

"Because I am always hungry," replied the toad.

"But you only eat earth!" exclaimed the charming insect. "Why do you not eat your fill?"

"Because one day," replied the miser, "even the earth might come to an end."

The Bull

(from the *Legend:* Pazzia. *H. 8 r.*)

An escaped bull was creating havoc among the flocks and herds. The shepherds no longer had the courage to take their animals to pasture because of this great savage beast who always appeared suddenly, charging with head down and goring everything that stood in his way.

The shepherds knew, however, that the bull hated the colour red, and so one day they decided to set a trap for him.

They draped the thick trunk of a tree with red cloth, and then hid.

The bull soon appeared, blowing through his nostrils.

Seeing the red trunk, he lowered his head to charge, and with a great crash his horns stuck in the tree, making him a prisoner.

The Walnut and the Bell Tower

(from the *Fable, Atl. 67 r.a.*)

A crow picked a walnut and carried it up to the top of a high bell tower. Holding the nut between his claws, the bird began to peck at it with his beak to open it. But the nut suddenly rolled down and disappeared into a crack in the wall.

"Wall, fair wall," begged the walnut, realising that it had been freed from the crow's fearful beak, "in the name of God, who has been so good to you, making you tall and strong, and enriching you with these fine bells that sound so beautiful, save me, have pity on me! I was destined to fall beneath my old father's branches," it went on, "and to rest in the rich earth covered with yellow leaves. Do not abandon me, I pray you. When I lay in the terrible beak of that fierce crow I made a vow. If God lets me escape, I said, I promise to finish my days in a little hole."

The bells, with a gentle murmur, warned the bell tower to take care, because the walnut might be dangerous. But the wall, moved to pity, decided to shelter it, and let it stay where it had fallen.

But in a short time the walnut began to open and to put roots through the cracks in the stone. Then the roots forced their way between the blocks of stone, and branches began to peep out of the hole. The branches grew, became stronger, and stretched up above the top of the tower. And the roots, thick and twisted, began to make holes in the walls, pushing out all the old stones.

The wall realised too late that the walnut's humility, and its vow to stay hidden in a hole, were not sincere. And it regretted not having listened to the wise bells.

The walnut tree went on growing and the wall, poor unhappy wall, crumbled and fell.

The Stone and the Road

(from the *Fable, Atl. 175 v.a.*)

Once upon a time there was a big and beautiful stone which had been smoothed by the water. After the water had gone, the stone remained exposed on fairly high ground at the very edge of a shady wood. From its position, surrounded by fresh and fragrant herbs and many-coloured flowers, it could see the stony road running below.

One day, looking at the road, on which a large number of pebbles had been thrown to harden the surface, it was overcome with longing to be down among them.

"What am I doing up here among these flowers? I want to live with my sisters. It seems only right that I should."

So saying, the stone moved and rolled down, ending its erratic course right in the middle of the pebbles whose company it so desired.

All sorts of things passed along the road—carts with iron-bound wheels, stamping horses, peasants with hobnailed boots, flocks and herds. The beautiful stone very soon found itself hard pressed. Some turned it over, some trampled it, some kicked it a short way. Sometimes it was smeared with mud.

Looking up at the place it had come from, the stone sighed for the loss of its solitude, and longed in vain for the peace it had once known.

This fable is for those who stupidly come from the peace and silence of the green countryside into the city, among people full of boundless evil.

The Cedar and the Other Trees

(from the *Fable, Atl. 67 v.b.*)

A beautiful cedar tree stood in a garden with many other trees. It grew taller every year, and its topmost branches stretched far above all the others.

"Take away that walnut tree," said the cedar, puffed up with pride at its own beauty. And the walnut tree was removed.

"Take away that fig tree," said the cedar. "It annoys me." And the fig tree was cut down.

"Get rid of those apple trees," went on the cedar, holding up its splendid head. And the apple trees were swept away.

So, one at a time, the cedar had all the other trees cut down, until it stood alone, master of the whole vast garden.

But one day a great wind came. The beautiful cedar fought against it with all its strength, gripping the earth with its long roots. But the wind, with no other trees to halt it, cruelly bent and battered the cedar, and finally, with a mighty crash, threw it to the ground.

The Falcon and the Duck

(from the *Fable, Atl. 67 v.b.*)

Every time he went duck hunting, the noble falcon was furious. Those ducks almost always succeeded in making a fool of him, diving under water at the very last moment, and remaining submerged longer than he could hover in the air waiting for them.

One morning, the falcon decided to try again. After circling for some time with outspread wings to review the situation, and carefully picking out the duck to be captured, the noble bird of prey dropped like a stone. But the duck was quicker, and dived head first.

"This time I'm coming after you," cried the falcon in fury, and dived as well.

The duck, seeing the falcon under the water, gave a flick of his tail, came to the surface, opened his wings and began to fly. The falcon's feathers were soaked, and he could not fly.

The ducks flew above him, saying:

"Goodbye, falcon! I can fly in your sky, but in my water you sink!"

The Flames and the Cauldron

(from the *Fable, Atl. 116 v.b.*)

In the midst of the warm ashes one ember still glowed. Very carefully, very thriftily, it was using up the remains of its strength, feeding only enough to keep itself alive.

But the time came to put the soup on the fire, and so fresh wood was thrown into the fireplace. A match, with its little flame, revived the ember which by now seemed dead. And a tongue of fire licked around the wood over which the cauldron had been placed.

Cheered by the dry logs that had been put on it, the fire began to rise, chasing away the air that slept between one piece of wood and another, and playing with the new wood. And it amused itself running over and under the wood, weaving in and out, and spreading more and more.

Then its tongues began to shoot outside the wood, opening many windows from which spurted showers of glowing sparks. The dark shadows fled from the kitchen. Meanwhile the flames grew more and more joyous, playing with the surrounding air, and beginning to sing with a soft sweet crackling sound.

And now the fire, seeing that it had grown up beyond the wood, began to change. Usually mild and quiet, it became proud and overbearing, imagining that it had bestowed the gift of flame on those few pieces of wood.

It began to breathe out clouds of smoke and to fill the hearth with explosions and showers of sparks. It flung its great flames upwards, determined to fly to heaven . . . and battered itself to extinction on the black bottom of the cauldron.

The Vine and the Old Tree

(from the *Fable. Ar. 42 v.*)

A vine, so as to feel safer, pressed close to an old tree. Its companions, which were clinging to the stakes which the vine-grower had planted in the earth for that purpose, asked it:

"Why have you chosen an old tree to support you? If it dies, what will you do?"

The vine, sure and satisfied with its choice, took no notice of its companions. It pressed closer and closer to the ancient trunk, certain it would live longer than all the other vines in the vineyard.

But the tree had lived for many years. It was so old that it could go on no longer. It shuddered at every gust of wind, and many of its branches were already dry and dead. At last, one day, it fell with a mighty crash and lay stretched out on the grass. The foolish vine, still embracing it, fell with it to the ground.

The Lion and the Lamb

(from the *Legend:* Umiltà *H. 11r.*)

One day a lion in a cage was given a little lamb to eat.

The lamb was so humble and innocent that he was not afraid of the lion, but crept close to him as though the lion were his mother, gazing at him with eyes full of devotion and wonder.

The lion, disarmed by such trusting innocence, had not the heart to kill the lamb. Grumbling, he remained with his hunger unsatisfied.

The Wine of Mahomet

(from the *Fable, Atl. 67 r.b.*)

Wine, that divine juice of the grape, was one day poured into a magnificent gold cup that stood on the table of Mahomet.

"Oh, what an honour!" thought the wine. "What glory for me to be on Mahomet's table!"

But suddenly a different thought occurred to it, and it said to itself:

"But what honour, and what glory? What am I so pleased about? None of this is true. What am I doing here? Look, I am about to die. I am about to leave my fine house, this magnificent golden cup, to enter the dark cavern of the human body.

"And once I am down there, my sweet fragrant juice will be transformed into water.

"Oh heavens!" it cried in despair, "grant me justice, grant me revenge for such an injury! It is not fair that I should be held in contempt like this! Jupiter, father Jupiter," it prayed, "if this land bears the best and most beautiful grapes in the world, grant that they are not turned into wine!"

Jupiter heard and decided to answer the wine's prayer.

When Mahomet had drunk from the golden cup, Jupiter made all the vapours of the wine rush to his head, so that he became drunk. And while he was in the grip of the wine, Mahomet behaved like a madman, doing one stupid thing after another. When at last he was himself again, he made a law forbidding any of his followers ever to drink wine.

From then on, the vine with its pleasant fruit was left in peace.

The Mole

(from the *Legend:* Bugia. *H. 9 r.*)

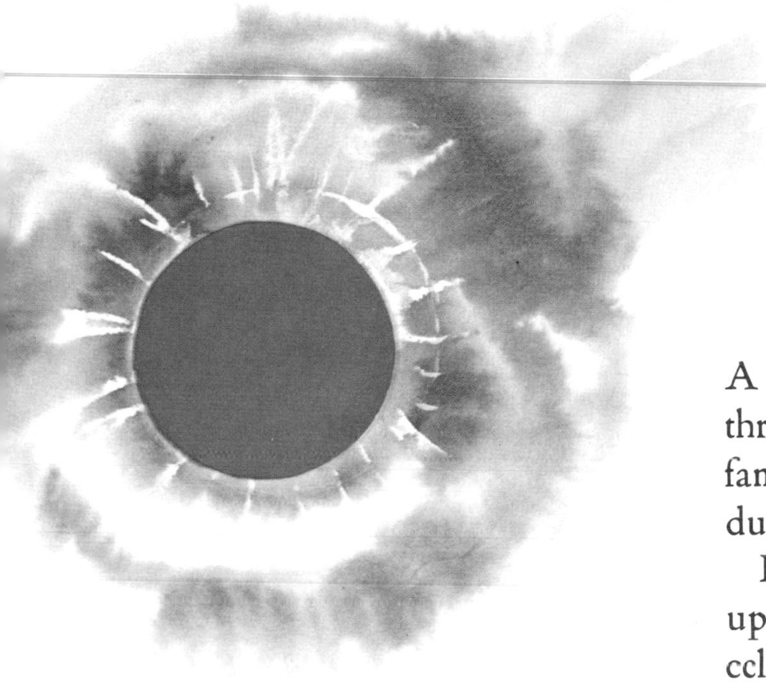

A mole was moving underground through the long galleries which his family had dug out and cleared during many years of work.

He went backwards and forwards, up to the top floor and down to the cellars as though he had perfect sight. Actually, like all moles, he had very tiny eyes and saw very little.

Finally he came to a passage he did not know, and continued his journey.

"Stop," called a voice from the floor below. "This corridor leads outside, and it is dangerous!"

But the mole went on upwards, until he found himself on a pile of newly turned earth.

He lifted up his muzzle and emerged. But the bright light of the sun blinded his eyes, and he scurried back to the hiding dark of his burrow.

Falsehood, like the mole, can live only if it remains hidden.

The Bear Cub and the Bees

(from the *Legend:* Ira. *H.* 6 *r.*)

A bear cub was wandering inquisitively through the forest when he saw a hole in the trunk of a tree.

Looking more closely, he saw that bees were constantly coming and going through the hole. Some were hovering in front of the entrance as though on guard. Some flew up from a distance and went in. Others came out and disappeared into the forest.

The bear cub, becoming more and more curious, reached up, put his nose to the hole, sniffed and then stuck in a paw.

When he pulled it out, his paw was dripping with honey.

But he had scarcely begun to lick it when a swarm of angry bees burst out of the hole and attacked him, stinging him on the nose, ears, mouth—everywhere.

The bear cub tried to defend himself, but if he drove them away on one side, the bees came back to the attack on the other. Infuriated, he tried to revenge himself by striking out at one and then the other. But trying to hurt all of them, he did not succeed in hurting any. Finally he rolled on the ground aimlessly until, overcome by terror and the pain of the stings, he fled crying to his mother.

The Willow and the Pumpkin

(from the *Fable, Atl. 67 r.b.*)

Once upon a time there was a poor willow that never had the joy of seeing its branches rising high into the sky. First there was a vine clinging to its trunk, then some other parasitic plant. There was always something to stop it from growing, and often it found itself broken and mutilated.

Mustering all its energy, the willow began to dream and then to think of the best way to free itself from this slavery.

It thought and thought again, one by one, of all the plants in the world around it, and the particular demands of each one, so as to find one at last that would never need to support itself on a poor willow's branches.

It brooded on this day after day, until at last an idea flashed upon its mind and it saw the light.

"Yes, of course—the pumpkin!"

The willow shook its branches in delight. The pumpkin really was the ideal companion, because it was more ready to prop up others than to be propped up itself. Having made its choice, the willow stretched its branches up to the sky in the hope that some friendly bird would notice it. At that very moment a magpie passed by. Immediately the willow called to him, and said:

"Sweet bird, I hope you have not forgotten the help I gave you a few days ago—it was one morning—when a cruel hungry falcon was trying to eat you, and you hid in my branches. And you remember, I hope, all the times you have rested on me when your wings were tired, and the pleasure you have had so often in my branches, playing with your companions. For all these things, sweet bird, I hope you will not refuse me the favour I am about to ask of you. Here it is. I beg you to go in search of a pumpkin, and ask it to give you a few of its seeds. And I shall tell these seeds not to be afraid of me. When their shoots are born, I shall treat them as though they were my own sons. I implore you," added the willow, "choose your words carefully. Persuade the pumpkin to give you the seeds and the seeds to come

with you willingly. You are a master of fine words, friend magpie, and I have no need to tell you what to do. If you will do me this great favour, I shall be glad to let you build your nest in my branches and to guard it, together with all your family, without asking you for any rent."

Then the magpie made a pact with the willow by which the latter promised most particularly not to allow either serpents or polecats among its branches.

Then he raised his tail and lowered his head, and dived from the tree, putting all his weight on his wings. Beating the swift moving air with rapid wings, and using his tail as a rudder to steer right and left, he came at last to a pumpkin.

"My respects to you," said the magpie to the pumpkin, "and my greetings."

He added many more fair and noble words, ending by asking for the seeds for which the willow longed.

When he had obtained the seeds he returned to his friend the tree, which welcomed him with joy.

"Now you must plant them," said the willow.

The magpie fluttered quickly to the ground, scratched the earth at the foot of the willow, took the seeds one by one with his beak and planted them round the trunk.

In a short time the seeds opened. The little pumpkin plants were born, and went on growing, putting out new branches that gradually imprisoned all those of the willow. Not only that, but the pumpkin plants with their great leaves hid from the tree all the beauty of the sky and the sun.

As if all that were not enough, when the pumpkins themselves appeared, their weight pulled the tips of the willow's tender shoots down towards the earth, tearing and torturing them. In vain the willow struggled and shook itself to dislodge the pumpkins. For days it twisted and turned in the belief that it was freeing itself. It was so desperate that it did not even realise that the pumpkins were tied to it with so many knots that no one could ever loosen them.

Seeing the wind pass, the willow screamed with pain and begged for help.

The wind heard, and blew harder.

Then the trunk, deprived of all nourishment by the pumpkins, split into two, right down to the roots. One part of the willow fell one way, and the other fell the other way, and weeping over its own misfortune, the willow concluded that it had been born under an evil star.

The Elm and the Fig Tree

(from the *Fable. Atl. 67 r.a.*)

A fig tree, laden with fruit which had not ripened and was still sour, looked up at a tree which was shading it, and saw that it had no fruit.

"Who are you, who dares to keep the sun from my little figs?"

"I am an elm," replied the tree.

"And you have not even one fruit!" went on the fig tree. "Are you not ashamed to stand in front of me? But wait until these children of mine are grown, and then you will see. Each one of them will become a tree, and together we shall make a forest and surround you."

And, indeed, the figs ripened. But when they were ripe, a company of soldiers passed. They climbed the tree to gather the figs, breaking the branches and leaves. Not one fruit was left, and the poor fig tree was left torn and maimed.

The elm, moved to pity, said:

"Oh fig tree, how much better it would have been for you not to have had children! You would not have built up such vain hopes. It is because of them that you are in this state now."

The Eagle

(from the *Fable, Atl. 67 v.b.*)

One day an eagle looked down from its high nest, and saw an owl.

"What a funny animal," he said to himself. "Surely it cannot be a bird."

Driven by curiosity, he opened his great wings and began to circle and fly down.

When he was near the owl, he asked:

"Who are you? What is your name?"

"I am the owl," quavered the poor bird, trying to hide behind a branch.

"Ha ha! how ridiculous you are!" laughed the eagle, still circling round the tree. "You are all eyes and feathers. Let's see," he added, settling on a branch, "let's see what you are like at close quarters. Let me hear your voice better. If it is as beautiful as your face we shall have to stop our ears."

The eagle, meanwhile, was trying with the help of his wings to make his way through the branches to catch the owl.

But a farmer had put twigs smeared with birdlime between the branches of the tree, and had also spread the largest branches with birdlime.

The eagle suddenly found his wings stuck to the tree, and the more he struggled to free himself the more entangled his feathers became.

The owl said:

"Eagle, the farmer will come soon, and catch you, and shut you in a cage. Or perhaps he will kill you in revenge for the lambs you have eaten. You, who spent your whole life in the sky, free from every danger, what need had you to come down here and make fun of me?"

The Monkey and the Baby Bird

(from the *Fable, Atl. 67 r.a.*)

One day a young monkey, leaping from branch to branch, saw a nest full of baby birds. Delighted, he approached and stretched out a hand to take them, but as they could already fly, they escaped, leaving only the smallest in the nest.

Happy as a king, the little monkey went home with the bird, and found him so charming that he began to kiss and caress him and press him to his breast.

"Be careful not to hurt him," said the mother monkey.

"But I love him!" replied the little monkey. "I love him so much."

And he went on kissing the baby bird and playing with him and hugging him, until finally he crushed him.

This fable is aimed at those who cannot punish their own children, and later suffer the consequences.

The Willow and the Vine

(from the *Fable. Ar. 42 r.*)

The willow is a tree with rapid and luxuriant growth. Its shoots lengthen visibly and are soon longer than those of any other tree.

But one day, for the sake of company, the willow decided to marry the vine.

"You're mad!" said a friend. "We willows are born to grow faster than any other tree. What will you do with a vine hanging on to you?"

But the marriage took place all the same. The willow joined with the vine, or rather allowed the vine to cling to its trunk.

But the vine bore fine bunches of grapes, while the willow had no fruit. And so one day, when the farmer found the vine entwined with the willow, he was afraid that the willow might pull it up out of the ground, and decided to prune both.

So, year after year, the willow's splendid shoots were cut back by the careful farmer, and the maimed and crippled tree served only to support the bunches of grapes belonging to its lucky companion.

The Crab

(from the *Fable, Ar. 42 v.*)

A crab noticed that many little fishes, rather than venture out into the river, preferred to swim prudently round and round a rock.

The water was as clear as the air, and the fishes swam peacefully, enjoying both sun and shade.

The crab waited until night, and when he was sure that no one would see him, he went and hid under the rock.

From this hiding place, like an ogre in his den, he watched the little fishes, and when they passed close to him, he seized them and ate them.

"That is not a nice thing you are doing," grumbled the rock, "making use of me to kill these poor innocents."

The crab did not even listen to the rock. Happy and contented, he went on catching the little fishes, which tasted delicious.

But one day there was an unexpected flood. The river swelled, and crashed with great force into the rock, which rolled over in the riverbed, crushing the crab hiding beneath it.

The Wine and the Drunkard

(from the *Fable, Fo. III. 21 r.*)

One evening a peasant, who had drunk more than he needed, said to his wife:

"Bring me another bottle."

"It is the last," replied his wife, handing him the bottle. "If you drink this, there will be none left."

"Good!" exclaimed the peasant. "I want to finish off all the wine we have in the house. I want to put an end to it forever."

And so he furiously gulped down one glass after another until the bottle was empty.

The wine was offended and decided to have its revenge on the drinker.

When the immoderate peasant went out into the farmyard to get a little air and cool the heat in his body, the wine made him stagger on his feet and sent him rolling into the mud.

The Swift

(from the *Legend:* Incostanzia. *H. 10 v.*)

The swallow, with loud and noisy cries of joy, returned to her old nest.

First she cleaned and tidied it, then laid her eggs. Then she sat on them. Finally, when her children had been born, she began to fly backwards and forwards, to and from the nest, to feed her large family.

The swift, on the other hand, simply flew all the time. She flew through the housework, and while her eggs were being hatched, and she was still flying every day, from dawn to dusk, without allowing herself a moment's rest.

"Why are you always flying?" she was asked one day.

"Because I don't like work," she replied.

The Cedar

(from the *Fable, Atl. 76 r.a.*)

Once upon a time there was a cedar that knew how beautiful it was.

It stood in the very middle of the garden, and was taller than all the other trees. And the absolutely symmetrical arrangement of its branches made it look like a great chandelier.

"Who knows what I should be like if I bore fruit?" it thought. "I should surely be the most beautiful tree in the world."

So it began to watch the other trees and try to do as they did. And at last, at the very tip of the tree, there grew a beautiful fruit.

"Now I must feed it," said the cedar to itself. "I must help it to grow."

And the fruit began to grow and swell until it was too big. The crest of the cedar could bear its weight no longer and began to bend. And when the fruit was ripe, the crest that had been the tree's pride and joy was left dangling like a broken branch.

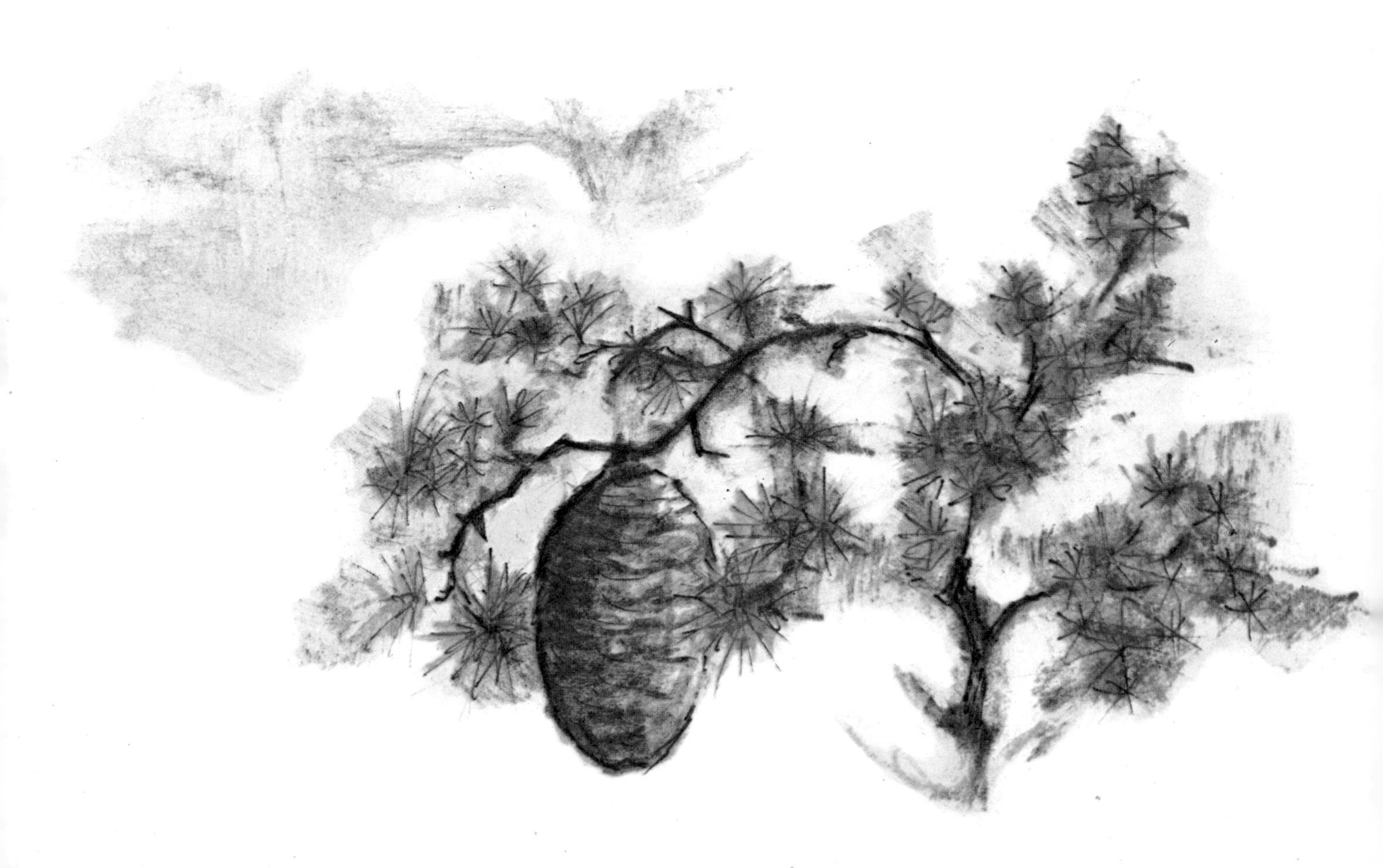

The Birds and their Instinct

(from the *Legend:* Verità. *H. 8 v.*)

Once upon a time there were two birds' nests in a garden. One was in a cypress and the other in an olive tree.

One day the bird who lived in the cypress stole an egg from the one who lived in the olive tree and added it to the eggs on which she was sitting.

After a while the eggs in both nests hatched and the two birds became mothers. Their children grew and became covered with feathers, and at last came the great day of their first flight.

One after the other, the baby birds from the olive tree flung themselves into space, fluttered around and returned happily to their nest.

One after the other, the babies from the cypress flung themselves down and fluttered round the garden. But one of them, instead of going back to the cypress, flew to the nest in the olive tree.

It was the bird from the stolen egg, instinctively returning to his real mother.

Happiness

(from the *Legend:* Allegrezza. *H. 5 v.*)

"Which is the happiest animal of all?" an old countryman was once asked.
"It is the cock," replied the countryman. "The cock is happiness itself. He rejoices when the day breaks, and he sings. He rejoices when the sun comes out, and he sings. He runs, leaps, fights and plays, singing all the time, happy and content, and the whole farmyard listens and rejoices with him."

Sadness

(from the *Legend:* Tristezza. *H.* 5 *v.*)

"And the saddest of animals?" the wise countryman was asked.

"The saddest of animals is the crow," he replied. "He is sadness itself. When the eggs hatch in the nest and the babies come out, the crow, seeing them so white and naked, is so heartbroken that he flees and abandons them. He flies away and weeps on a neighbouring tree. Then at last he sees that the first feathers are beginning to appear on their skin, and then he comes back."

The Crocodile and the Ichneumon

(from the *Legend:* Coccodrillo: Ipocresia. *H. 17 r.*)
(Icneumone e coccordrillo. *H. 25 v.*)

A crocodile killed a man who was sleeping under a palm tree, then wept bitter tears over him.

"You see," said an ichneumon to his son, "the crocodile is a hypocrite, for he is weeping now, and before long he will devour his victim."

And in fact, after a while the crocodile began calmly to eat his prey.

After his meal he went to sleep on the river bank with his mouth open, so that a bird called the crocodile bird, with which he was friendly, could get into his mouth and pick out the remains of food from between his teeth.

His digestion pleasurably aided by the industrious bird, the crocodile opened his powerful jaws wider in his sleep.

Then the ichneumon said to his son:

"Now watch carefully, and learn. The crocodile has a strong armour, and his sides are protected against me. But this is how traitors are killed."

And taking a run, he hurled himself into the crocodile's mouth, and bit him through the throat.

The crocodile awakened with a start, and began to roll on the ground, howling with pain. At last, destroyed by the ichneumon, he lay belly up, dead as a stone.

The Walnut Tree

(from the *Fable, Atl. 76 r.a.*)

In a garden surrounded by a high wall, many fruit trees lived together. Each one was covered with blossom in spring and loaded with fruit in summer. And with them there was also a walnut tree.

"Why should I hide myself away in this garden?" said the walnut tree one day. "I am going to stretch out my branches as far as the road, so that everyone can see how rich my fruit is."

And so, a little a time, it stretched its fairest branches over the wall so that everyone could see them.

But when its boughs were loaded with nuts, wayfarers began to pick them, and when they could not reach them with their hands, they pulled them down with sticks, and if they could not manage with sticks they threw stones.

In a short time the walnut tree, beaten and stoned, lost both fruit and foliage, and was left with its poor broken arms hanging down over the wall.

The Thrushes and the Owl

(from the *Fable, Atl. 117 r.b.*)

"We are free! We are free!" cried the thrushes one day, seeing that a man had caught the owl.

"Now the owl will frighten us no more. Now we shall sleep in peace."

The owl had in fact fallen into an ambush, and the man put him into a cage.

"Let us go and see the owl in prison," said the thrushes, flying and singing around their enemy's cage.

But the man had captured the owl for another purpose—to catch the thrushes. In fact, the owl at once allied himself with his captor, who tied him by one foot and put him well in view on a trestle every day. In order to see him, the thrushes flew on to the neighbouring trees, in which the man had hidden sticks covered with bird lime. And the thrushes lost their liberty just like the owl.

This fable is directed at all those who rejoice when an oppressor loses his freedom. For the conquered soon becomes the ally or the tool of the conqueror, while all those who depend on him fall beneath another master, and lose their liberty and often their lives as well.

The Spider and the Hornet

(from the *Fable, Atl. 67 v.b.*)

A spider happened to find himself in a place frequented by flies. At once he set to work weaving his web. He chose two branches for support, and began to scurry to and fro between one and the other. Spinning his silver thread, he built his spider's web. When his work was complete, he hid behind a leaf.

His wait was short. A curious fly soon became entangled in the web. Out rushed the spider and ate the fly.

But a hornet had seen everything from his position on a flower. He immediately flew at the spider and pierced him with a sting.

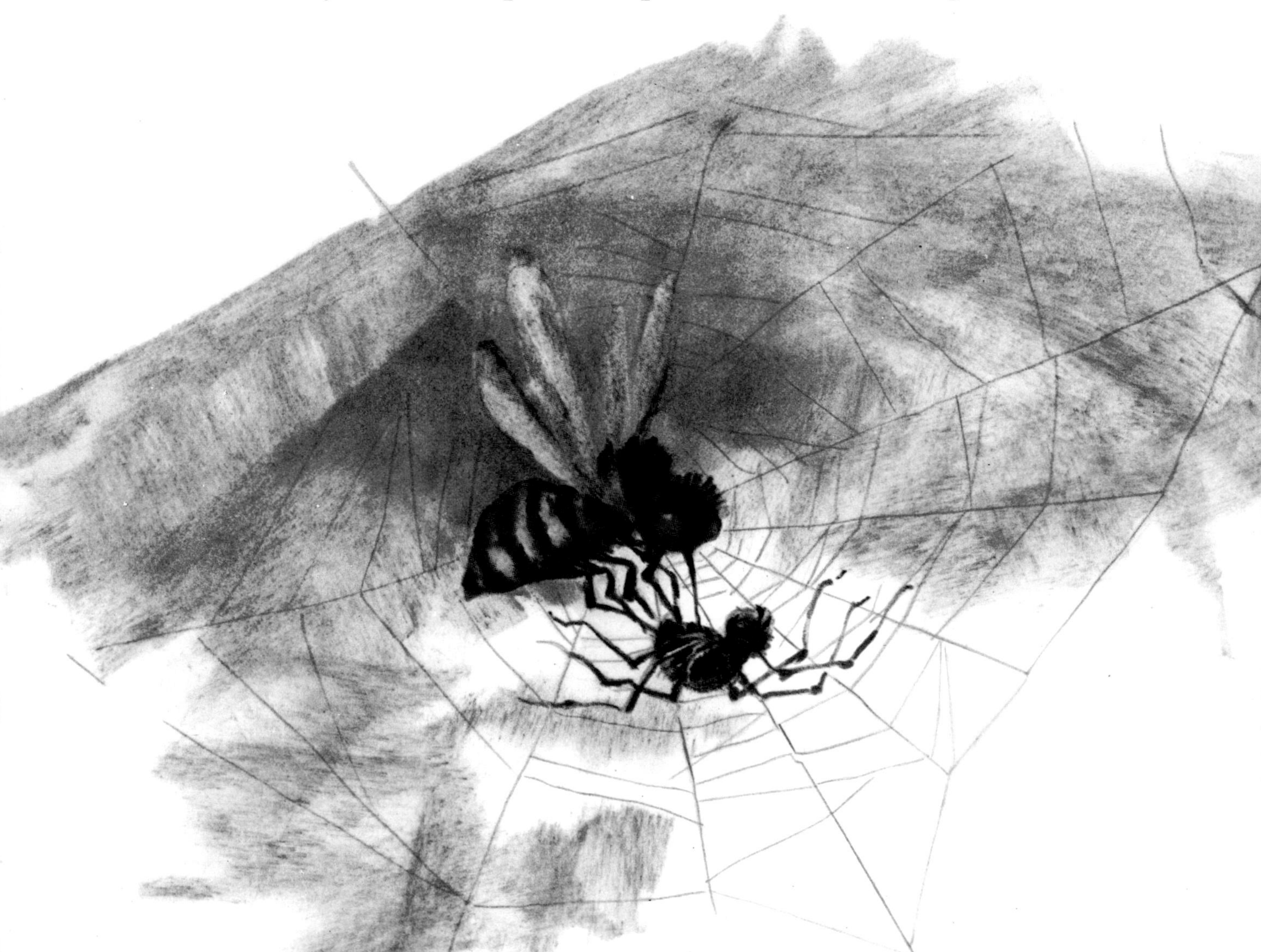

The Snake and the Birds

(from the *Legend:* Serpenti. *H. 21 r.*)

There were no longer so many birds in the flock as there had been before. Each day one of them disappeared mysteriously without any of the others noticing. The leader of the flock could find no explanation.

One morning, instead of flying ahead, he put himself at the tail of the flock so that he could keep a watchful eye on his companions.

As usual they flew towards a distant wood. As they passed over a hill, the leader noticed that the orderly flock fell apart, as if struck by a strong wind. Most of the birds at once got back into line. But two of the youngest continued to go the wrong way as if they were being pulled by an invisible force.

And suddenly, the leader of the flock saw the snake. He was very long, with many coils.

Every morning he waited, hidden in the grass, for the birds to pass. He would open his mouth and pull in his breath, sucking the birds between his jaws.

Having discovered the danger, the wise leader took his flock a different way on the following days, and the snake caught no more.

The Caterpillar

(from the *Legend:* Bruco—Della virtu in generale. *H. 17 v.*)

Sitting still on a leaf, the caterpillar looked around him and saw all the insects in continual movement—some singing, some jumping, some running, some flying. Poor creature, he was the only one that had no voice and could neither run nor fly.

With a great effort, he began to move, but so slowly that when he passed from one leaf to another he felt as though he had been round the world.

And yet he envied nobody. He knew he was a caterpillar, and that caterpillars have to learn to weave fine threads, with wonderful skill, until they have made themselves a little house.

And so he eagerly began his work.

In a short time the caterpillar was enclosed in a warm silk cocoon, shut off from all the rest of the world.

"And now?" he wondered.

"Now wait," replied a voice. "Still a little patience, and you will see."

At the right moment the caterpillar awoke, and was no longer a caterpillar.

He came out of the cocoon with two beautiful brightly coloured wings, and at once flew high into the sky.

The Unicorn

(from the *Legend:* Intemperanza. *H. 11 v.*)

The hunters spoke of the unicorn as a mysterious creature.

"Is he an animal or a spirit?" they wondered.

Indeed, this strange little horse with a horn in the middle of his forehead appeared now here, now there, yet no one ever managed to take him by surprise.

"Wild and strange," said the hunter, "perhaps a messenger from Hell, sent to earth to spy on us."

"No, he is too beautiful to be an evil spirit. He must be an angel," replied another.

A young girl, sitting apart beneath an arbour, listened in silence, spinning her wool, and smiled. She knew the unicorn well, she knew all about him.

He was her friend.

And in fact, when the men had gone, the animal appeared from behind a bush, and ran to the girl. He lay down beside her, rested his muzzle in her lap, and gazed at her with eyes full of love.

After the first meeting, he became as tame as a domestic animal, stretching out his muzzle for a kiss.

But this strange love was his ruin.

The hunters realised what was happening, and one day, without the girl knowing, they lay in ambush and caught the innocent unicorn.

The Testament of the Eagle

(from the *Legend:* Aquila. *H. 12 v.*)

Many years ago, a majestic old eagle lived alone on top of a very high mountain. One day he sensed that the hour of his death was not far off. With a mighty cry he summoned his sons who lived lower down the mountain. When they were all gathered together, he looked at them one by one, and said:

"I have provided for you and brought you up so that you might look directly at the sun. Those of your brothers who could not tolerate the sun's face I have allowed to die of hunger. For this reason, you deserve to fly higher than all the other birds. Any who want to preserve their lives will not attack your nest. All the animals will fear you and you shall never harm those who respect you. You shall allow them to eat up the scraps of your prey.

"Now I am about to leave you. But I shall not die here in my nest. I shall fly very high, as far as my wings will carry me. I shall stretch out towards the sun to take my leave of it. The sun's fiery rays will burn my old feathers. I shall fall towards earth and finally into the water.

"But miraculously I shall rise again from the water, rejuvenated and ready to begin a new existence. Such is the lot of eagles, our destiny."

With these words the eagle took to the air. Majestic and solemn he flew round the mountain where his sons stood. Then, suddenly, he turned upwards towards the sun which would burn up his tired old wings.

Example of the reverse writing
or "mirror writing" used by
Leonardo da Vinci.

Right : the manuscript
Left : reflected in a mirror

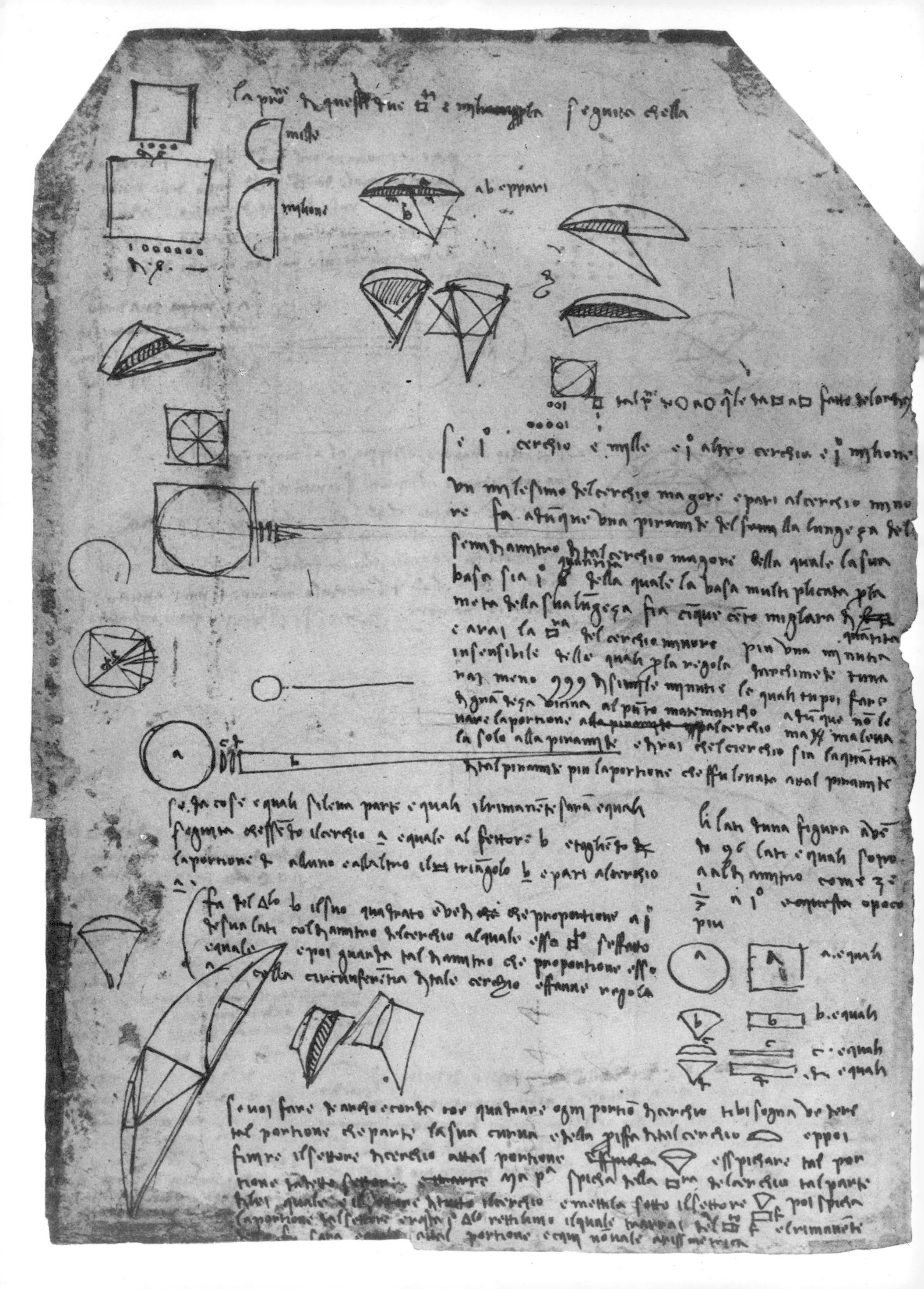

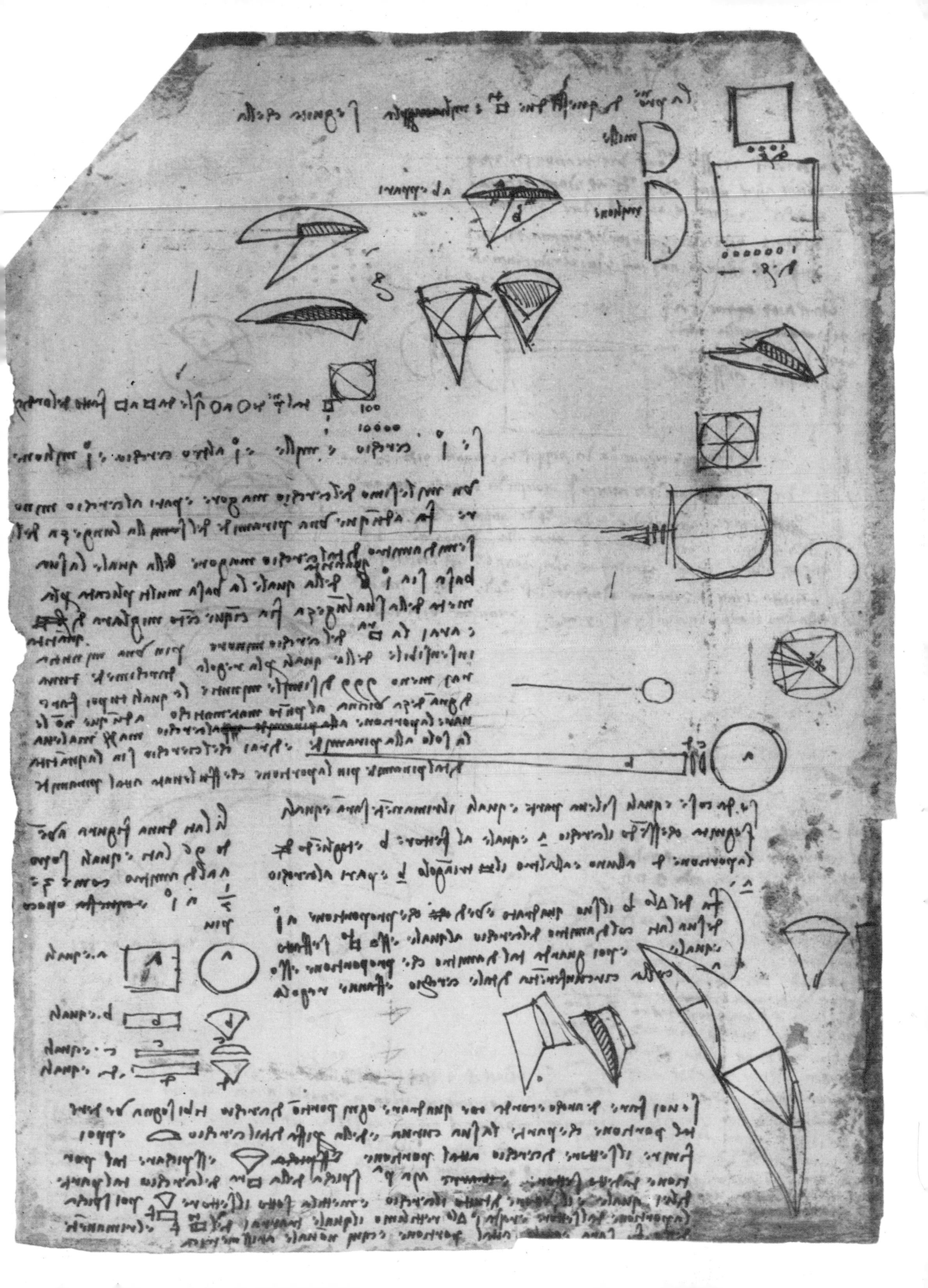

The typeface used in this book is Monophoto Poliphilus.
It is a copy of a roman type cut by Francesco Griffo
for the Venetian printer, Aldus Manutius, in 1499.
It is an exact facsimile of Aldus's printed sheet.

KEY TO REFERENCE ABBREVIATIONS

Atl. — Atlantic Code — Located in the Biblioteca Ambrosiana, Milan, Italy

Fo. — Foster Code — Located in the Institut de France, Paris, France

H. — Humbert Code — Located in the Institut de France, Paris, France

r. — facing page

v. — reverse page

The numerals in the references refer to the page, and the alphabetic references following "r." or "v." refer to a specific section.

[illegible]

[illegible]

[illegible]

[illegible] propria vita . [illegible]

[illegible] la libertà [illegible]

[illegible]

[illegible] la libertà [illegible]